A Song Abou

by Mary Tucker

Tune: "This Old ...

1 Jesus Christ, God's own Son,
Baptized by His cousin John,
To fulfill God's plan and show the world His love.
Jesus came from heav'n above.

2 Jesus Christ did not sin
When the devil tempted Him,
To fulfill God's plan and show the world His love.
Jesus came from heav'n above.

3 Jesus Christ, God's own Son,
Healed the blind and deaf and dumb,
To fulfill God's plan and show the world His love.
Jesus came from heav'n above.

4 Jesus Christ taught God's Word,
Showed us how to please the Lord,
To fulfill God's plan and show the world His love.
Jesus came from heav'n above.

5 Jesus Christ helped His friends,
Calmed a storm and stopped the wind,
To fulfill God's plan and show the world His love.
Jesus came from heav'n above.

6 Jesus Christ, raised the dead,
And fed a crowd with fish and bread,
To fulfill God's plan and show the world His love.
Jesus came from heav'n above.

7 Jesus Christ came to town.
Cheering people gathered 'round,
To fulfill God's plan and show the world His love.
Jesus came from heav'n above.

8 Jesus Christ died and then
He came back to life again,
To fulfill God's plan and show the world His love.
Jesus came from heav'n above.

9 Jesus Christ said goodbye
As He went into the sky,
To fulfill God's plan and show the world His love.
Jesus came from heav'n above.

Taken from the *Life of Jesus Time Line Poster Set*.
ISBN 0-382-30491-8

Ten Commandments

You should not desire

Copy the ten commandments' blossoms and flowerpots on different colors of paper. Place them on a table in scrambled order. Have children match the pieces and glue them on a piece of poster board. They may then draw stems from the flower pots to the flowers.

what others have.

You should have no other gods

You should not make any idols

You should not misuse the name

before Me.

for yourself.

of the Lord your God.

Remember the Sabbath Day

Honor your father

You should not

by keeping it for God.

and your mother.

murder.

You should not be unfaithful

You should not

You should not

to your mate.

steal.

speak lies.

(Teacher's Note: The commandments have been written in simple language to help students understand them.)

by Joanne R. Willanger

34

CELEBRATE EASTER

by

Kelly Riley

illustrated by Vanessa Filkins

Music by:
Helen Kitchell Evans, Frances Mann Benson, Grace Click,
Kathy Jones and Kelly Riley

Cover by Dan Grossmann

Shining Star Publications, Copyright © 1987
A Division of Good Apple, Inc.

ISBN No. 0-86653-385-0

Standardized Subject Code TA ac

Printing No. 9876543

Shining Star Publications
A Division of Good Apple, Inc.
Box 299
Carthage, IL 62321-0299

Unless otherwise indicated, the New King James version of the Bible was used in preparing the activities in this book.

A WORD TO PARENTS & TEACHERS

Easter is a season of new life—the eternal life Jesus won for us by His suffering, death and resurrection. The flowers, eggs, bunnies and chicks traditionally associated with Easter are all symbols of new life. Encourage the children to think of Easter as a time of new life too, as a time to give the gift of new life to ourselves and others. Each time we reach out to another in love, we bring new life to ourselves as well as to them. As an Easter project, the children might keep a "New Life" journal in which they jot down their thoughts and feelings about the season, ways they have grown or reached out to others, special Scripture verses and prayers, choices they have had to make as followers of Jesus—anything that has been meaningful and "life-giving" to them during this special season.

Celebrate Easter is designed to help you and the children learn more about Jesus' last week on earth, and in so doing, grow in faith, love and understanding yourselves. Integrated into the Scripture lessons are a variety of bulletin boards, stories, music, creative writing, memory verses, discussion topics, craft projects and recipes to help make Easter more meaningful for all. Fourteen coloring pages are also included that can be assembled into an Easter book. Everything needed for an Easter musical—songs, script, costume ideas—are found in the last chapter of the book.

NOTE: The source for passages and verses used in this book is The New King James Version of the Bible. Much of the dialogue in the culminating Easter pageant is drawn from the Good News Bible.

Rejoice and celebrate,

Kelly Riley

DEDICATION

Celebrate Easter is dedicated to all my former students. A special note of thanks goes to Kathy Gronski and Helen Remaly, children's librarians at McMillan Memorial Library in Wisconsin Rapids, WI, for their unselfish aid and support in all my writing endeavors.

SS842

TABLE OF CONTENTS

SONGS

EASTER COLORING BOOK PAGES

Shining Star Publications, Copyright © 1987, A division of Good Apple, Inc.

SS842

EASTER ANTICIPATION

Each day, starting forty days before Easter, choose a flower and read the Scripture verse in your Bible. Then color the flower.

John 13:34

I John 4:7

John 15:12

John 13:35

Ephesians 6:24

Luke 6:27

I John 4:19

II Corinthians 13:11

I John 4:12

Luke 6:32

Mark 9:37

Luke 6:37

Revelation 1:18

John 3:15

John 1:11,12

Romans 6:11

Luke 11:28

Mark 9:41

I Peter 4:8

John 7:33

Romans 10:7

Luke 12:8

Luke 14:27

John 20:29

Romans 4:5

II Corinthians 5:7

Hebrews 10:36

Hebrews 11:1

John 12:44,45

John 15:13

John 11:25

I John 5:13

Proverbs 8:35

John 7:38

John 1:4

John 10:10

John 6:33

Philippians 1:21

John 10:9

John 10:28

Shining Star Publications, Copyright © 1987, A division of Good Apple, Inc.

SS842

THE KING COMETH

Now when they came near Jerusalem . . . He sent out two of His disciples . . . "Go into the village opposite you; and . . . find a colt tied, on which no one has sat . . . ."

Then they brought the colt to Jesus . . . and He sat on it. And many spread their garments on the road, and others cut down leafy branches from the trees and spread them on the road . . . and those who followed cried out, saying:

"Hosanna! Blessed is He who comes in the name of the Lord! Blessed is the kingdom of our father David That comes in the name of the Lord! Hosanna in the highest!"

Mark 11:1-10

In Old Testament times, the palm tree was a symbol of the rulers of Israel. In Jesus' time palm branches were used as a sign of victory. The idea of placing palm branches on the path before a king or hero originally came from the Romans. Whenever the Romans were victorious in battle, the people would lay palm branches along the path of the returning heroes.

This was the accepted custom of reception among the Jews during Jesus' life. The Jewish people expected the Messiah to be an earthly king who would free them from the Romans. When Jesus rode into Jerusalem, the people welcomed Him by laying down cloaks and branches. They waved palm branches to show that He was their hero.

SS842

JEROD AND THE KING

"Hurry, Jerod," Adar tugged excitedly at his older brother's hand, "Father said a king is coming!"

"A king?" Jerod wondered to himself as he swung Adar up onto his shoulders and scampered down the hillside to join their father. "Could it be the one they call the Son of David?"

As they joined the hundreds of people making their way toward the city of Jerusalem, Jerod thought back to all the stories he had heard about kings. He tried to imagine what this new king would look like. In his mind, he could see the king dressed in purple robes, a golden crown atop his head, riding a magnificent white war horse. He thought about the soldiers who would accompany the king and the people blowing trumpets and waving banners in his honor.

"Who is this king?" Jerod asked his father as they made their way through the crowded city.

"He is the Messiah," his father answered, placing his hand on his older son's shoulder. "Today he will come to Jerusalem to reign as the King of the Jews."

"Look, Father," Adar pulled at his father's robe to get his attention, "everyone is picking palm branches."

"Yes, little one," Father smiled down at his youngest son. Then he broke off several branches and handed one to each of the boys. "When the Messiah comes, lay these branches on the road in front of him. It is our way to welcome him."

Suddenly there was a cry of delight from the crowd at the gates of the city. "Here He comes! Here comes the King!"

Jerod edged closer to the front of the crowd lining the roadside. His heart beat excitedly at the thought of seeing the King for the first time. Adar crept closer to his brother, waving his palm branch happily as he gazed in wonder toward the gates of the city.

As the cry of "Hosanna! Hosanna in the highest!" rang through the crowd, Jerod caught his first glimpse of the rider passing through the city gates.

"Why, he is not a king at all," Jerod thought sadly. "He's just an ordinary man riding a donkey." The shouts of "Hosanna!" grew louder. People began laying cloaks and palm branches on the path.

SS842

As the rider passed in front of the two boys, Adar crept onto the path. He laid his palm branch on the road. Then, looking up at the man, he timidly whispered, "Hosanna!"

The man on the donkey paused for a moment. He smiled gently and laid his hand on Adar's head as if in blessing. For a brief instant, a crown of light encircled the man's head. Then he continued on his way.

Jerod could hardly believe what he had seen. He looked around to see if anyone else had noticed the light, but the faces in the crowd showed no surprise. "Maybe he is a king after all," Jerod thought to himself as he watched the rider disappear into the crowd.

WELCOME, JESUS

Imagine how excited the people were when they heard that Jesus was seen coming up the road to Jerusalem. They welcomed Him as they would a king by laying cloaks and palm branches in His path and offering words of praise.

Ask the children to suggest ways we might welcome Jesus if He came today. Provide a variety of materials, and have each child create something (for example: banner, button, poster, balloon) that he or she could use to publicly show his or her faith in Jesus. Perhaps the children might use their creations for Palm Sunday church services.

THINKING ABOUT THE STORY

1. In the story, Jerod wonders if the king could be "the one they call the Son of David." Who was David?
2. What kind of king does Jerod think he will see in Jerusalem?
3. Who does Father say the new king is?
4. How do the people welcome the king?
5. What word did the Jewish people use to worship God?
6. Why do you think they used this word to greet the new king?
7. How do you think Jerod felt when he saw Jesus at first? Why?
8. What does Adar do when he sees Jesus?
9. Why does Jerod think that Jesus is just an ordinary man?
10. Why does Jerod say "Maybe he is a king after all," at the end of the story?

A DONKEY FOR A KING

Have the children read Matthew 21:2 and Mark 11:2 to discover what kind of animal Jesus told His Disciples to find. Ask the children to suggest reasons why Jesus chose a donkey. Through discussion lead the children to see that Jesus chose to ride a donkey to show the people that He was not the kind of king they expected Him to be. The donkey is a symbol of Jesus' humility (He wasn't carried on a litter as befits a king), His peacefulness (He didn't enter Jerusalem as a conqueror riding a war horse), and His identification with the common people (the donkey was the animal of the people). Some children might recall that a donkey was associated with Jesus' birth. Mary rode a donkey to Bethlehem, and a donkey carried the Baby Jesus to safety in Egypt. Ask the children to suggest reasons why Jesus chose an unridden colt. (To show that His mission was a sacred one.)

CHRIST'S KINGSHIP

Ask the children to imagine that a new king is coming to their town. Have them draw pictures showing what they expect to see when the king arrives. Have the children suggest words and phrases that would show the qualities they expect in such a king. If the new king is not what they expect him to be, how will they feel?

The Jewish people expected Jesus to be a powerful leader. They knew that He had worked many miracles. They were not surprised to see Him ride into Jerusalem on a donkey, because the Prophet Isaiah had foretold that the Messiah would arrive that way. But Jesus did not fulfill their expectations. He did not summon a great army of angels and drive the Romans from power. Jesus was not an earthly king. Have the children suggest words and phrases they could use to describe Jesus' kingship. Have them work in groups to find a way to show Jesus' qualities as a king. They might put on a skit, pantomime Jesus as a king or act out the words and phrases—as in charades—that describe His kingship.

 SS842

... BEHOLD, YOUR KING IS COMING TO YOU, LOWLY, AND SITTING ON A DONKEY .... Matthew 21:5

OBJECTIVE: To visually represent Christ's triumphant entry into the capital city of Jerusalem on Palm Sunday.

MATERIALS: Pale blue poster paper, an enlarged colored picture of Jesus riding a donkey, gold letters, and palm leaves in various shades of green.

PROCEDURE: Cover the bulletin board with pale blue poster paper. Pin the picture of Jesus riding a donkey on the left side of the board. Pin the letters in place. Discuss the fact that although Jesus is truly a king, He is not a king in a worldly sense. He did not arrive in Jerusalem with all the pomp and glory of a worldly king. Instead He entered the city humbly like a common man. Yet the people greeted Him with cries of ''Hosanna'' and lined His path with cloaks and palm leaves. Ask the children to imagine that they were in Jerusalem on that first Palm Sunday. What words of praise would they have used to honor the arrival of the king? Have each child write the words of praise of his or her choice on a palm leaf and sign the leaf. Have the children pin their palm leaves on the bulletin board to line Jesus' path.

SS842

SWAY THE PALMS

For the Jewish people, the palm tree has always been a tree of honor and a symbol of hope and life; so it was fitting that they honored Jesus by waving palm branches. Today, Palm Sunday services help us remember Jesus' triumphant entry into Jerusalem and prepare us for the celebration of Easter joy. When Jesus entered Jerusalem, the people did not know about Easter and the kind of eternal life Jesus would win for them. They did not remain faithful to Him during His last week of life. As you sing this song, think about the ways you can remain faithful to Jesus in your life.

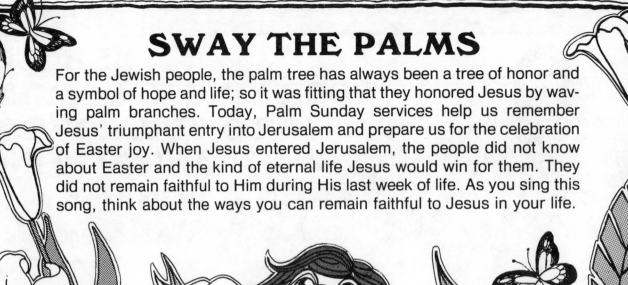

Words and Music by Helen Kitchell Evans
Frances Mann Benson

Sing ho-san-na to the King As He-brews did long a-go. Let voi-ces low-ly ring prais-ing our Re-deem-er and our Heav'nly King to-day. Sway palms, sway palms as of old Let the great Sto-ry be told. Sway, Sway the palms be-fore Je-sus As He-brews did long a go.

SS842

PALM BRANCH— CREATIVE MOVEMENT

When children have learned the song on page 10, they might enjoy planning some creative movements to accompany their singing. If the children are interested, let them create some motions of their own, or teach them the simple routine below. The children might perform the song and plan movement (with the pastor's permission) as a part of the Palm Sunday service. Real palm fronds or ones cut from heavy paper can be used in the movement.

To begin, the children stand in a line and clasp hands. Place the palms on the floor in front of the children.

SING HOSANNA . . . Step to the left, dipping slightly; close with right foot; release hands.

TO THE KING . . . Step to the right while bringing both arms, palms facing out, in an arc from left to right. Close with left foot about halfway through arc.

AS HEBREWS DID LONG AGO . . . Step back with left, then with right, standing with feet apart and crossing arms over chest. Open arms out to the side and slightly down with palms out.

LET VOICES LOUDLY RING . . . Turn quarter turn to the right, and raise arms overhead, looking up.

PRAISING OUR REDEEMER . . . Turn quarter turn to the left, kneel on one knee, and extend hands outward.

AND OUR HEAVENLY KING TODAY . . . Pick up palm fronds and stand.

SWAY PALMS, SWAY PALMS AS OF OLD . . . Extend both arms out to the left side (holding palm frond in each hand); bring arms up in an arc to the right side, then to the left in time to the music.

LET THE GREAT STORY BE TOLD . . . Step back with left foot, close with right foot, and lift arms and palm fronds high. Bring arms down on the word "told."

SWAY PALMS, SWAY PALMS BEFORE JESUS . . . Repeat the movements from the same line above.

AS HEBREWS DID LONG AGO . . . Step forward with right foot; kneel on left knee; place palm fronds on the floor in front of you and cross your hands over your heart.

SS842

PALM TREE FACTS

The palm tree mentioned in the Bible is actually a date palm. The date palm was probably the first tree grown by man. More than 5000 years ago, the people of Mesopotamia made bricks on which they carved directions for growing the date palm tree.

Look at the sentences below. Unscramble the numbered words to discover some facts about date palm trees.

A date palm tree (1) WRSOG _____ 40 to 100 feet high. The (2) KRUTN _____ is straight and tall. A crown of large leaves shaped like (3) HASERTEF _____ grows on top. For the first four to ten years of its life, a date palm cannot bear (4) TUFIR _____. When the tree is old enough, small (5) WLROFES _____ grow among the leaves. Each flower soon becomes a (6) TEAD _____. The dates grow in clusters of as many as 200. Each cluster can weigh up to 25 (7) SOPNUD _____. Inside each date is a long, tough (8) DESE _____ that can grow into a new date palm tree. On the tree the dates have a red or golden (9) ROOLC _____. (The ones we eat are brown because they have been (10) REDID _____.) A date is about one inch (11) GOLN _____ and tastes (12) WESTE _____. Date palm trees grow where it is dry and hot. (Bring in some dates for students to taste.)

SS842

STAND-UP PALM TREE

Follow these directions and make a palm tree of your own.

TRUNK: For the trunk you will need an 8″ x 3½″ piece of wood-grain Con-Tact paper. Remove one inch of the backing along a long side and a short side. Roll the paper into a tall cylinder, so the sticky side of the paper overlaps the other edge of the cylinder. Cut four one-inch slits around the bottom of the trunk. Fold out the tabs and stick them to a cardboard base.

LEAVES: Cut an 8″ square of green construction paper. Cover it with an 8″ x 9″ sheet of clear Con-Tact paper. (One inch of the clear contact paper should be sticking out below the bottom edge of the construction paper.) Cut slits from the top to about one inch from the bottom of the paper. Cut the slits a half-inch apart. Make each leaf pointed if you wish. With the sticky side out, roll the green paper into a cylinder. Place it inside the trunk, pressing the sticky contact along the inside of the trunk near the top. Fold down the leaves.

PALM BRANCH PLAQUE

Crossed palm branches are a symbol of Christ's kingship. You might like to make a plaque to remind you of Jesus' triumphal entry into Jerusalem on that first Palm Sunday.

Cut a 9″ x 12″ sheet of yellow tagboard or cover cardboard with yellow construction paper. Cut two leaves from 4½″ x 11″ sheets of green construction paper. Glue a green pipe cleaner down the center of each leaf so that one inch of the pipe cleaner shows as a stem. Fringe each leaf to look like a feather. Bend the leaves to give them a realistic, three-dimensional look. Place the leaves in a crossed position on the tagboard. Glue the bottoms and tops of the leaves in place.

Cut a 3″ x 6″ strip of white paper. Roll the ends to look like a scroll. Print a Bible verse of your choice (or use the one below) on the scroll. Glue the scroll near the top of the tagboard above the palm leaves. Glue a pop-top ring to the back of the plaque so it will be easy to hang.

Blessed is the King who comes in the name of the Lord! Peace in heaven and glory in the highest!
Luke 19:38

SS842

PALM SUNDAY PRETZELS

At one time, particularly in Austria, Germany, and Poland, pretzels were a special food that was only eaten during Holy Week. In these European countries, the word *pretzel* was spelled *brezel*. It comes from the word *brachiatus*, which means ''having branch-like arms.''

The shape of the pretzel resembles the shape of a person with his arms folded in prayer.

Pretzels were first made in the fifth century by monks in Rome and were distributed to poor people on certain days before Easter. For many years this was the only bread eaten from Wednesday through Saturday of Holy Week. Because the dough was twisted to represent two arms crossed in prayer, pretzels reminded the people of the reverence associated with the Easter season.

In Austria, pretzels could be purchased from a street vendor called a ''Brezelmann'' on Palm Sunday. The pretzels were then hung on palm branches as part of the Palm Sunday celebration.

It is only in the last century that pretzels have been available all year long.

BREAD PRETZELS

1¼ cups warm water (105° to 115°)
1 package active dry yeast
½ teaspoon sugar
4½ cups sifted flour
1 egg yolk
1½ tablespoons milk
coarse salt

Dissolve the yeast and the sugar in the warm water. Let it stand for one hour. Mix in the flour. Knead the dough for seven or eight minutes. Place the dough in a greased bowl. Cover it with a towel and let it rise until it is double in size. Form the dough into pretzels. Place the pretzels on a greased cookie sheet. Mix the egg yolk and milk together, and brush it over each pretzel. Sprinkle generously with coarse salt. Allow the pretzels to rise until not quite double in size. Bake in a preheated oven at 475°F for about 10 minutes. The recipe yields eleven 6-inch pretzels.

Pretzels can also be made using commercially-prepared cans of refrigerated bread stick dough. Shape the bread stick dough into pretzels. Brush each pretzel with the egg yolk/milk mixture and sprinkle with coarse salt. Bake according to the directions on the package.

SS842

JESUS CLEANSES THE TEMPLE

Then Jesus went into the temple of God and drove out all those who bought and sold in the temple and overturned the tables of the moneychangers and the seat of those who sold doves. And He said to them, ''It is written, 'My house shall be called a house of prayer, but you have made it a den of thieves.' '' Matthew 21:12,13

Jesus' first act after arriving in Jerusalem was to go to the temple. For Jesus and His followers, the temple was the religious center of their community life, just as our churches are important to our lives as part of a Christian community.

SS842

JESUS IN THE TEMPLE

Read Mark 11:15-17. Then read the story below. The numbered words in the story are printed backwards. Rewrite them the correct way.

In Jesus' time people had to travel many (1) SELIM _____ to the temple in Jerusalem. In the temple they offered (2) STFIG _____ of sheep, cattle and doves on the altar to show that they were God's (3) NERDLIHC _____. Because they had traveled so far, they did not bring the (4) SLAMINA _____ with them. Instead they (5) THGUOB _____ them in Jerusalem. Usually the people had to go to a moneychanger to get their (6) SNIOC _____ changed for ones used in the city. Sometimes the animal sellers and moneychangers (7) DETAEHC _____ the people.

When Jesus entered Jerusalem on (8) MLAP _____ Sunday, He went to the temple. He found that the moneychangers and the men who sold animals for the (9) SECIFIRCAS _____ had set up their (10) SPOHS _____ in the temple. The temple looked more like a (11) TEKRAM _____ place than a place to (12) PIHSROW _____ God. This made Jesus very angry.

Even though He was only one man, the people recognized His (13) REWOP _____ and fled in panic. Then Jesus (14) EVORD _____ the animals out of the temple and tipped over the (15) SELBAT _____ of the moneychangers. Then He told them, ''In the (16) SERUTPIRCS _____ God said, 'My temple will be called a house of (17)REYARP _____ for the people of all (18) SNOITAN _____.'''' Then He made them leave the (19) ELPMET _____.

Shining Star Publications, Copyright © 1987, A division of Good Apple, Inc.

SS842

REBUILDING THE TEMPLE

After Jesus drove the moneychangers and the merchants out of the temple, the Jewish authorities asked Him, ''What miracle can you perform to show us that you have the right to do this?''

Jesus answered, ''Tear down this temple, and in three days I will build it again.''

The Jewish authorities did not understand how Jesus could possibly rebuild the temple in such a short time. ''Are you going to build it again in three days?'' they asked Him. ''It has taken forty-six years to build this temple!''

The Jewish authorities and the disciples did not understand what Jesus was saying. What do YOU think Jesus was telling them? To find out what Jesus meant, follow the line below from dot-to-dot and write the words on these lines.

_____

_____

_____

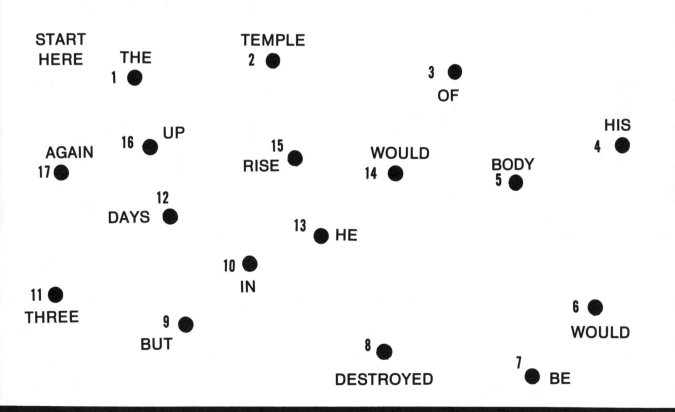

START
HERE   THE   TEMPLE
             1   2 ●   3 ●
                                                           OF

                      UP   HIS
              16 ●   15 ●   WOULD   4 ●
AGAIN   RISE   14 ●   BODY
17 ●   5 ●

        12 ●
DAYS
                        13 ● HE

              10 ●
              IN

11 ●   6 ●
THREE   9 ●   WOULD
             BUT
                                 8 ●
                        DESTROYED   7 ● BE

SS842

SPRING CLEANING TIME

Do you not know that you are the temple of God and that the Spirit of God dwells in you?   I Corinthians 3:16

Jesus cleansed the temple in Jerusalem by driving out the moneychangers and the men who sold doves and other things. Discuss Jesus' reason for doing this and why the things these men were doing were wrong.

In I Corinthians 3:16 Paul tells us that each of us is a temple of God because the Lord lives in us. Each spring many mothers give their homes a thorough cleaning. Spring is a good time for each of us to clean out the things that clutter our hearts so that we can be fitting temples for the Spirit of God.

Each of the cobwebs below spells out something we should clean out of our lives. To discover the hidden words, change each letter to the letter that comes before it in the alphabet. Then write each word on the line below.

GET TO KNOW YOUR HOUSE OF PRAYER

Look at the picture of Jesus in the temple. Hidden in the picture are some things that might be found in a church today, but would not have been found in the temple of Jerusalem. Circle each thing. Can you find all six? (The answers can be found on page 144.)

TAKE A TOUR

Make arrangements with your pastor to take your students on a tour of your church. Even though the children may attend church services frequently, there is much they do not know about the church. Take the children to places in the church that they may never have seen before. Visit the choir loft, youth room and other places. Ask the pastor to explain special things about the church to the children, such as the vestments and special items used in worship, as well as how he prepares for the Sunday service.

ART ACTIVITIES

Have the children work in groups to create a clay model or painting of your church. Other groups might create a symbol or seal or make rubbings of raised or depressed designs or symbols found on the pulpit, altar, doors, and other places within the church. Others might draw a map showing places in the world where your church is active. Encourage the children to work together.

Shining Star Publications, Copyright © 1987, A division of Good Apple, Inc. SS842

THE HOUSE OF WORSHIP

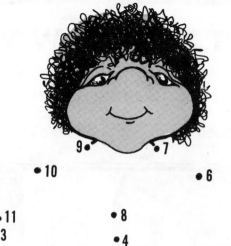

God tells us that His house should be a house of worship. How do you think children in Jesus' time worshipped God? Connect the numbered dots in this picture. Then connect the dots marked with letters. What do you think the boy is doing?

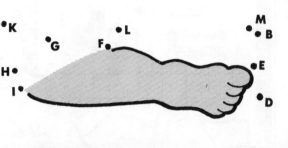

MANY WAYS TO WORSHIP

There are many ways to worship God. Look at each picture below. What way of worship is shown in each picture? Write your answers on the lines below the pictures.

SS842

OBJECTIVE: To visually represent the concept that the church is not just a building. It's the people who worship God who are the real temple of the Lord.

MATERIALS: Pale blue poster paper, bright yellow letters, an enlarged drawing of a white church and green trees, white construction paper, crayons or markers for student use, and scissors.

PROCEDURE: Cover the bulletin board with pale blue poster paper. Pin the letters and the picture of the church in place. Give each child a 6″ x 9″ sheet of white construction paper. (If children are very young, you might wish to provide them with an outline pattern of a boy or girl.) Have the children make colored paper dolls of themselves. Encourage the children to try to make their paper dolls look as much like themselves as possible. Have the children memorize II Corinthians 6:16 (minus the first sentence). As each child learns the verse, have him put his paper doll in the church on the bulletin board.

THE CHURCH IS PEOPLE

. . . For you are the temple of the living God. As God has said, "I will dwell in them and walk among them. I will be their God and they shall by My people."

II Corinthians 6:16

MANY MEMBERS

If your church has more than one Sunday service, the children may not realize how many members there are. With your pastor's approval, place construction paper strips at the entrance to your church. Ask that each person attending services print his/her name on a strip. Collect all the strips and have the children make a paper chain for display in the church. Discuss what it means to be members of a church.

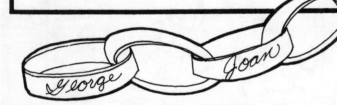

WORKING TOGETHER

The church is people working together. Have the children work together to create a large mural showing people involved in various church activities. Display the mural to welcome visitors to your church.

GALLERY OF CHRISTIANS

Encourage the children to find out about famous people who led prayerful lives. Ask each child to draw one of his favorite Christians on a sheet of paper and to write a few lines about the person. Display the drawings in a Gallery of Christians.

FINGER PLAY CHURCH

When Christians join hands, it's like
    (Clasp hands together, fingers in palms)
A church with a steeple.
    (Index fingers touch and point up)
For the temple of God
    (Spread thumbs apart)
Is really His people.
    (Turn hands upward to show all the fingers)

(The actions are the same as those of the old finger play entitled "Here is the Church.")

CHRIST OUR CORNERSTONE

Now, therefore, you are . . . fellow citizens with the saints and members of the household of God, having been built on the foundation of the Apostles and Prophets, Jesus Christ Himself being the chief cornerstone, in whom the whole building, being joined together, grows into a holy temple in the Lord.

Ephesians 2:19-21

The cornerstone is a stone that unites two walls at the corner of a building. When important buildings are constructed, the cornerstone is the first stone laid. Usually a ceremony takes place, and an important person in the community is given the honor of setting the stone in place. A cornerstone is often inscribed with a date and/or a significant phrase or sentence. Frequently the cornerstone is made into a repository for documents and other significant things. Talk to your pastor and find out what, if anything, is in the cornerstone of your church. Help the children locate your church's cornerstone and discuss its importance. Ask the children to suggest things they would want to put in a cornerstone if they were building a church.

Paul tells us that we are part of a holy temple in which Jesus is the cornerstone. The temple is not one constructed of real blocks, but of faith. To help the children understand the importance of a cornerstone, have them make paper lunch-bag bricks. Cut 2½-inch slits in the corners of the open ends, fold in and seal shut. Write the name Jesus on one bag and the names of the children on the others. Build two walls in which the block with Jesus' name is the cornerstone. Talk about what would happen to the walls if we removed the cornerstone. What would happen to our faith if we removed Jesus?

SS842

TEMPLE GRAFFITI

''He who overcomes, I will make him a pillar in the temple of My God . . . And I will write on him the name of My God . . . .'' Revelation 3:12

What names do you call our Lord when you talk to Him? What words of praise do you use when you pray?

Fill the pillar at the left with as many names for God or Jesus and as many words or phrases of praise as you can think of. Include small drawings of things that remind you of the Lord, too.

SS842

MARY OF BETHANY

And when Jesus was in Bethany . . . a woman came to Him having an alabaster flask of very costly fragrant oil, and she poured it on His head as He sat at the table.

But when His disciples saw it, they were indignant, saying, "To what purpose is this waste? For this fragrant oil might have been sold for much and given to the poor."

But when Jesus was aware of it, He said to them, "Why do you trouble the woman? For she has done a good work for Me. For you have the poor with you always, but Me you do not have always. For in pouring this fragrant oil on My body, she did it for My burial." Matthew 26:6-12

Bethany is located in Jordan, about two miles east of Jerusalem. Its modern name is el Azariya. Jesus frequently visited the small village of Bethany to see His friends Mary, Martha and Lazarus. Mary is a good example of someone who gave unselfishly. She placed more value on Jesus' needs than she did on material things. Mary could have chosen to anoint Jesus with olive oil or some other less costly perfume. Instead she sacrificed both the fragrant oil of spikenard and the precious alabaster box in which it was contained.

Shining Star Publications, Copyright © 1987, A division of Good Apple, Inc.

SS842

JESUS VISITS BETHANY

Use the picture clues and fill in the missing words in the story. The following picture clues are provided:

 BETHANY **JESUS** **LAZARUS** **MARY** **MARTHA**

 _____ had three friends who lived in a village called _____. Their

names were _____. _____ and _____. _____

loved to visit their _____. It was there that _____ raised

_____ from the dead, and there that  _____ sat at his _____ listen-

ing while _____ was so busy in the _____. _____ liked to

go to _____ when He needed rest and quiet. Before He died, _____

went to visit His friends. He sat at a _____ with _____.

 _____ served them a meal. _____ took a _____ of costly

perfume. She poured it on his _____ and wiped them with her

_____. One of the Disciples got very angry because the perfume cost 300

_____. But _____ knew that _____ did this to show how much she

loved Him.

 SS842

REACH OUT

So let each one give as he purposes in his heart, not grudgingly or of necessity; for God loves a cheerful giver.

II Corinthians 9:7

When Mary of Bethany sat at Jesus' feet and listened to Him, and when she anointed Him with the oil of spikenard, she was putting Jesus' needs ahead of her own. When Jesus returned to Jerusalem for the Passover celebration, He knew it might be dangerous for Him to do so because the Jews had tried to stone Him earlier. Yet He went, despite the risk, because His friends needed Him. The Gospels teach us that when we dwell on our own importance, we are far away from God's love; but when we serve the needs of others, His peace and love are by our side.

POSTER POWER

Easter season has traditionally been a time of sacrifice and doing something for God. Have the children discuss some ways in which they might focus on the needs of others while they make personal sacrifices in their own lives. List these ways on the board where the children can see them. Then have each child design a poster that illustrates a way that we can put others' needs ahead of our own. Each poster might also include an appropriate Bible verse about giving. Display the posters where other children and members of the congregation can see them.

FOR I WAS A STRANGER . . .

Read Matthew 25:34-40 to the children. Discuss the idea that Jesus taught us that we should give food to the hungry, drink to the thirsty, and clothing to the naked. We are to welcome the stranger, visit the sick, and minister to those in prison. Divide the class into three groups and have each group concentrate on how they can carry out Jesus' teachings about reaching out to the stranger, the sick and the imprisoned. Possible actions could include writing letters to prisoners, sending cards to the sick, and helping a refugee family adjust to American life.

SS842

"... Freely you have received, freely give." Matthew 10:8

BOX MOBILES

During the Easter season, some people traditionally give up something (like candy or another treat or activity they would miss) as a kind of sacrifice. Suggest to the children that it might be a better idea to give oneself as Christ gave Himself to us. Encourage the children to respond to the needs of others and to work at building meaningful relationships with people they are around daily. Discuss the ways children can reach out to others—the unpopular child who needs a friend, the crossing guard or bus driver who could use a friendly smile or kind word, the teacher who would appreciate a peaceful recess duty, the janitor or school cook who is sometimes taken for granted. Have the children illustrate ways they could reach out to these people. On sheets of paper cut to fit various boxes (cereal boxes, cracker boxes, etc.) create box mobiles with drawings and appropriate Bible verses.

BUILDING BRIDGES
Bulletin Board

Unselfish giving comes about when we are able to see Jesus in our neighbors. When we recognize Christ in others, we are able to reach out to them and create bridges to close the gaps between ourselves and other people. Paint individual-serving size cereal boxes to resemble bricks. On one side of a bulletin board put pictures of happy children; on the other side put pictures of people in need of something. Encourage the children to notice when someone reaches out to another. Children can add a brick to the bulletin board each time, creating a visual "bridge" of sharing and giving.

"... Freely you have received, freely give."

THE POOR WITH YOU

When Mary anointed Jesus with the costly oil of spikenard, some of the Disciples who were there became angry. ''Why was this fragrant oil wasted? For it might have been sold for more than three hundred denarii and given to the poor . . .''

But Jesus said, ''Let her alone. Why do you trouble her? She has done a good work for Me. For you have the poor with you always, and whenever you wish you may do them good; but Me you do not have always.''

Mark 14:4-7

Jesus teaches us that we have a responsibility to the poor. Most children today are aware that there are poor throughout the world, but they (like us) often forget that there are poor right in our own communities. Lead the children in a discussion about the poor in your city. Who are they? What kinds of things do they need? What is being done to help them? Ask the children to suggest ways they can help the poor in their own community.

Decorate a large box with pictures of the poor and appropriate verses from the Bible about giving. Emphasize that the poor need our help in many ways. Encourage the children to suggest some ways they could make helping the poor an on-going project throughout the school year, not just an occasional donation of something the children don't need. Ask them to suggest some things that might be put into your classroom ''poor box'' at different times. For example, one month the children might contribute canned goods or take up a clothing collection for a needy group. September might be a good time to contribute school supplies for needy children. Toys could be collected at Christmastime, particularly if there is an organization (like the firemen) who make repairing and distributing toys a yearly project. At other times children might make some things for the needy (for example, a picture-word scrapbook of American items for a refugee child).

Holidays can be especially unhappy times for the poor. To help make holidays a little brighter, churches and other organizations sometimes sponsor free dinners for the needy. Encourage the children to contribute their time and talents to help make such a project a success. Children might volunteer to help set up chairs, run small errands for the group in charge, provide entertainment or help with cleanup.

BOX PUPPETRY

Turn a large box into a puppet television stage by cutting an opening (the screen) in the bottom of the box. Paint it to resemble a TV set, complete with channel selector and dials. Set the TV puppet theater on a table for use during the skits. Older children might enjoy preparing a TV guide to inform the class about their skits. Include time, channel, and a brief plot summary or "blurb" to stimulate interest.

Simple puppets can be made from small boxes, such as those from a cereal variety pack. Use a serrated knife to cut through the middle of the box (as shown in the diagram) leaving one side as a hinge for the mouth. Have children paint the boxes with tempera paint to which a few drops of liquid soap have been added to help the paint adhere to the box. Provide scraps of fabric, felt, buttons, yarn, paper, pipe cleaners, etc., which children may use to create faces and other features to make puppet personalities. For example, buttons may be used for eyes, pipe cleaners for whiskers, and yarn or fake fur for hair. Group the children in twos or threes, and have them create puppet skits showing examples of unselfish giving. A child can manipulate the puppet's mouth by placing the fingers in the top and the thumb in the bottom half, then opening and closing fingers and thumb.

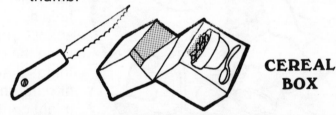

CEREAL BOX

"ME" BOXES

God has provided each of us with many blessings and talents. Think about the ways you can reach out to others and minister to their needs. Cover the top of a box with white paper. Find a verse in your Bible about giving. Neatly letter the verse on the white paper. (Some possible verses include Acts 20:35, Acts 3:2-6, II Corinthians 9:7, Matthew 5:42, and Matthew 10:8.) Cut pictures from magazines that illustrate ways you can live daily according to the verse you have chosen. Glue the pictures to the four sides of the box in a "caring" collage. Display your box for others to see.

"My peace I give to you." John 14:27

SS842

THE WIDOW'S MITE

The Bible tells a story about a woman who gave unselfishly. Read this story, based on Mark 12:41-44, to the children. A group of children might act out the story in pantomime or use box puppets like those on page 30 to dramatize the story while you read it.

One day near the end of Holy Week, Jesus and His Disciples rested on some steps near the Temple. Across the courtyard from them was the Temple treasury. In front of the treasury were thirteen alms boxes in which the people could place their offerings to help carry on God's work. Each box was labeled so the people would know what their money would be used for. Many people had come to Jerusalem for the Passover, and Jesus and His friends watched as the people made their offerings to God.

As the people brought their offerings to the Temple, the priest placed their money in the alms boxes so that all the people could see how much their neighbors had given. As Jesus and His Disciples watched, several rich men came to make their offerings. Each man contributed a large amount of money to help the Temple priests carry out the work of the Lord.

A poor widow entered the Temple area to place her offering into the alms boxes. The widow's offering was small, only two small copper coins that together were worth about one-eighth of a cent, but it was all that she could afford. When the widow gave her offering to the priest, he threw the coins into a box and loudly announced the amount of the offering so that all could hear. The Temple priest and the crowd of people looked at the widow with such contempt that the poor woman became embarrassed and ran out of the Temple.

Jesus, to make sure His friends did not miss an important lesson, turned to His Disciples and said, ''I tell you that this poor widow put more into the offering box than all the others.''

Ask the children what Jesus meant when He said that the poor widow had given more than all the rich men had given. When the children have had a chance to express their opinions, turn to Mark 12:44 and read Jesus' words. Help the children to understand that Jesus was not talking about the amount of money that each gave, but how much each had to sacrifice to make an offering.

Ask the children to think about some times when they or others they know have treated someone like the priest and the crowd treated the poor widow, for example, a child who gives a friend a used toy as a birthday present, a child who brings penny candy as a treat when everyone else has been bringing candy bars, etc. How does Jesus want us to treat such children? Guide the children in understanding that what may be a big sacrifice for one child may not seem to be much of one to other children. Jesus judges the spirit in which a gift is given, not the gift itself.

SS842

BEAUTIFUL BOXES

Mary anointed Jesus with a fragrant oil made from the roots of the spikenard plant. This perfume was usually imported into Palestine in alabaster (a precious stone) boxes. Make an attractive box using one of the ideas below, line it with a plastic bag, and fill it with potpourri. Give the box to someone you love.

ALUMINUM FOIL BOX

A beautiful box can be created with string and aluminum foil. Cut thin cardboard pieces the exact size of the top and sides of your box. Draw an attractive design on each piece of cardboard. Glue string to each piece, following the design. Cut pieces of foil about two inches longer and wider than the cardboard section. Spread glue thinly and evenly over the aluminum foil and place it over the string design. Press the foil into the depressions around the design. Then glue the overlapping ends to the back of the cardboard. Finally glue each section to the box and allow it to dry. Metallic cord can be glued along the edges of the box to give it a finished look.

MOCK ALABASTER BOX

Alabaster was a precious stone somewhat like white marble. To make a pretty white box, paint a recipe box or cigar box. Cut some designs from the top of a white styrofoam egg carton or a styrofoam meat tray. Glue the designs on the top and sides of the box. Emboss some of the designs with a toothpick or flat stick if you wish. A protective coat can be added to the box by spraying it with hair spray. (Do not use lacquer, as it will eat into the styrofoam.)

NOTE: Only the Gospel of John identifies the woman who anointed Jesus as Mary. Matthew and Mark identify the home as being that of Simon, rather than Lazarus, and do not name the woman.

Shining Star Publications, Copyright © 1987, A division of Good Apple, Inc.

SS842

THE LIGHT OF THE WORLD

Then Jesus said to them, "A little while longer the light is with you. Walk while you have the light, lest darkness overtake you; he who walks in darkness does not know where he is going. While you have the light, believe in the light, that you may become sons of light." These things Jesus spoke, and departed, and was hidden from them. John 12:35,36

Jesus calls Himself the light of the world. Jesus was associated with light. For example, a star shone over the stable the night of His birth; a light as the dove (Holy Spirit) descended on Him at His baptism; a white light surrounded Him at His transfiguration; His Resurrection was at sunrise; an angel surrounded in brightness told the women that Jesus had arisen; and He appeared to His Disciples at dawn by the seashore after His Resurrection.

SS842

LET THERE BE LIGHT

Then God said, "Let there be light"; and there was light. And God saw the light, that it was good; and God divided the light from the darkness. God called the light Day, and the darkness He called Night. So the evening and the morning were the first day. Genesis 1:3-5

Of all the things God created for us, light is the most important. Light from the sun makes life on Earth possible. Have the children suggest some ways light is important to us. Some points to consider include

Light provides our food. Plants need sunlight to grow. All animals, including man, eat plants or plant-eating animals.

Light allows us to breathe. As plants grow they give off oxygen to the air. We need to breathe oxygen to stay alive.

Light allows us to see. Without light, the world would be totally dark, and we would not be able to see anything.

Light warms the earth. Without sunlight, the earth would be so cold that nothing could live on it.

Genesis 1:3-5

Without light, we could not live. Yet we seldom stop to think how important it is. We often take light for granted. Jesus came as a light to the world. Do we take Jesus for granted too? Have the children suggest some ways or times they think they take Jesus for granted.

Ask the children to think about some of the ways Jesus brought light to the world. With younger children, you might have them discuss some ways as a group. Ask each child to draw a picture showing Jesus as the light of the world. Display the completed pictures in a "Light of the World" gallery for all to enjoy. Older children might enjoy writing free verse (nonrhyming) poems entitled "Jesus is my Light" to accompany their pictures. Perhaps your pastor would publish some of the children's poems in the Sunday bulletin during the Easter season.

SS842

TO MAKE THE BLIND SEE

For a blind person, the world is a dark place. There is no light. It's difficult for those of us with sight to imagine what it is like for the blind, but children can experience blindness to some degree by doing a trust walk. Have the children pair off in twos. One child in each pair is blindfolded. The other child then takes the blindfolded child for a walk. No talking is allowed. The leading child must help the blindfolded child to avoid obstacles and to experience the world around him by using his other senses (touch, sound, smell.) Form a sharing circle to discuss the experience, particularly the way things changed for the blindfolded child.

Braille is a form of printing for the blind that uses raised dots. Working from the back of a heavy piece of paper, use a pin to make a series of raised dots to spell out a name. Ask the children to close their eyes. Then give each a paper and have him use his sense of touch to determine whose name he has.

JESUS CURES THE BLIND

On at least five different occasions, Jesus cured the blind. Divide the children into five groups. Assign each group a different Bible passage: Matthew 9:27-31; Matthew 12:22,23; Mark 8:22-26; Mark 10:46-52; John 9:1-12. Allow time for each group to prepare and perform a short skit based on the assigned passage. (With younger children you might prefer to read John 9:1-12 and one or two other passages to them.) Discuss the ways Jesus brought light to His blind followers.

KIND OF BLINDNESS

For those of us with the gift of sight, the ability to see is often taken for granted. But there are other kinds of blindness besides physical blindness. Sometimes we are blind to what happens around us. We do not really look at things, or we see only what we want to see. Ask the children to recall some times when they are "blind." (For example, not seeing when we hurt someone by words or actions, ignoring others when they need us, pretending that something unpleasant doesn't exist.) Discuss what it means to see things "in a new light." Ask the children to try to see their daily lives in a new light for a week. Have them keep a journal in which they note things they had not really seen before. Provide time for sharing at the end of the week.

Jesus refers to Himself as the light. He came to give sight to the blind, to bring light to those who live in darkness. Talk about how sinning and refusing to choose Jesus' way are kinds of darkness. How does Jesus help us chase away the darkness so we can live in the light?

SS842

BRIGHT IDEAS

HANGING SUN

Enlarge the sun pattern at the right. Cut two suns from two different colors of construction paper. Cut slit to the center from the top of one sun and from the bottom of the other. Slip one sun over the other at a right angle. Anchor with tape.

Have the children find verses about light in their Bibles, using a concordance, or choose from those below. Print a verse on the left half of one section and its biblical reference facing it. Do this for the other three sections as well. Thread a string through the top of each sun and hang the suns around the room.

Possible verses include

Matthew 5:16	Luke 8:16
John 12:46	I John 2:10
Isaiah 9:2	Psalm 27:1
Matthew 5:14	Psalm 43:3
John 1:4	I John 1:5
John 8:12	John 9:5.

LAMP BOOKMARK

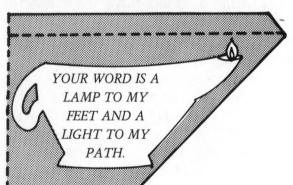

YOUR WORD IS A LAMP TO MY FEET AND A LIGHT TO MY PATH.

PLACE ON FOLD

EASTER CANDLE

JOY

To make an attractive Easter candle, paste white tissue paper over a white candle. Cut an oval of white tissue paper to fit halfway around the candle and about two-thirds its length. Use waterproof markers to draw Easter symbols or to print words like ''Alleluia'' or Bible verses on the tissue. Brush the candle with diluted white glue on the area the tissue will cover. Carefully smooth the tissue paper onto the glued surface. Brush a coat of glue over the tissue paper.

Short, wide candles about two inches in diameter work best, but tall tapers can also be used.

To make this corner bookmark, duplicate the pattern on heavy paper that is twice as wide as the pattern. Fold along the fold line and cut out. Trim ¼ inch off the top of the left side (the side without the lamp). Fold along the dotted line and glue the flap in place. Add color to your bookmark.

SS842

"LIGHT" BULLETIN BOARD

Cover the bulletin board with black or dark blue poster paper. Cut the letters from bright gold paper and pin them in place. Provide colored construction paper or copies of the candle pattern (enlarged to size desired) and markers so each child can make a candle for the bulletin board.

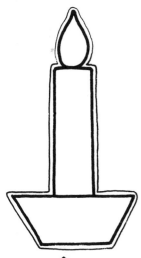

When God created us, He gave each of us special talents. We can use our talents to help others grow in love and kindness. Tell the children that the candles stand for each of them. Have them print their names on the bases. Ask each child to print on the candle a way he can share in bringing Jesus' light to others. Pin to board.

WINDOWS

Fold a 3½" x 5" sheet of white construction paper in half. Fold a sheet of black paper of equal size in half and slip it inside the white paper. Draw half a church window on the fold on the white paper. Cut out the openings, being sure to cut through all four layers. Open the papers and position the white window over the black so it overlaps. Glue in place. Glue a sheet of colored tissue paper to the back. Trim off any excess. Hang your window in the light. Talk about how light changes the appearance of the window. We are changed too when the light of Jesus' love shines through us.

SUNSHINE SMILES

Duplicate a large number of the sun patterns on bright yellow construction paper. Cut them out. Print "Have a sunshine day!" on a sun for each child. The children can wear them as badges. Talk about how Jesus calls us to help spread the light of His love to everyone. Ask the children to do things for each other to make the day sunnier. Each time a child feels someone has brought some sunshine into his life, he draws a smiley face on a sun and sticks it up somewhere in the room. See if your classroom can be full of "sunshine smiles" by the end of the day.

SS842

FESTIVAL OF LIGHT

In Isaiah 60:2 the Prophet Isaiah foretold that a deep darkness would cover the earth and that the Lord would send a great light to the people. The darkness Isaiah talked about is sin and death. Jesus came as a light to the world to bring us the light of His love and salvation. Jesus told us that we too must be lights to the world. This activity celebrates Christ as the light of the world.

MATERIALS:
Paschal candle (see below)
Vigil light (or candle from craft activities)
   for each child
Base for a large candle
Copy of script and song for each child
   (pp. 39—41)
Action card (see page 42) for each child
Song—"You Are the Light of the World"
   (GODSPELL Album)
Long matches

PREPARATION:
Place the Paschal candle on a base so that it rises above the other candles. Arrange the vigil lights (or candles) around the base of the Paschal candle. Light the Paschal candle and lower the lighting in the room. (Be sure the children have practiced their parts and the song beforehand.)

PASCHAL CANDLE

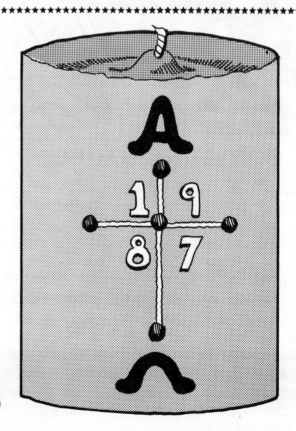

Use a large white candle to make the Paschal candle. Using a heated knife, carve the first and last letters of the Greek alphabet and a cross on the candle. Use a mixture of tempera paint and egg yolk to paint the carved areas (or fill them in with melted, colored wax.) Place five cloves in the candle at the points shown in drawing. Use sticker numerals to add this year's date. (They can be replaced easily for following years.)

Discuss the symbols used on the candle with the children.

The Paschal candle is usually lighted the night before Easter. Use it for prayer time.

SS842

CHORAL READING—HE IS OUR LIGHT

CHILD 1:	The people who walked in darkness have seen a great light.
BOYS:	They lived in a land of shadows,
GIRLS:	But now the light is shining on them.
ALL:	You have given us great joy, Lord. You have made us happy.
CHILD 2:	Long before Jesus was born, God spoke to His people through the prophet Isaiah. He said,
BOYS:	Arise, and shine like the sun.
GIRLS:	The glory of the Lord is shining on you!
BOYS:	Others will be covered by darkness,
ALL:	But on you the light of the Lord will shine.
GIRLS:	The brightness of His appearance will be with you.
CHILD 3:	No longer will the sun be your light by day,
CHILD 4:	Or the moon be your light by night.
ALL:	I, the Lord, will be your eternal light!
CHILD 5:	The light of my glory will shine on you,
CHILD 6:	More lasting than the sun and moon.
ALL:	I, the Lord, will be your eternal light!
CHILD 7:	Before He died, Jesus told His Disciples,
CHILD 8:	I am the light of the world.
CHILD 9:	Whoever follows me will have the light of life and will never walk in darkness.
ALL:	The Lord is our eternal light.
BOYS:	The light shines in the darkness for those who are good,
GIRLS:	For those who are merciful, kind, and just.
CHILD 10:	Jesus died to overcome the darkness of sin and rose to be our light.
CHILD 11:	Jesus wants us to bring His light to others. He tells us,
GIRLS:	Your light must shine before people,
BOYS:	So that they will see the good things you do,
GIRLS:	And praise your Father in Heaven.
ALL:	Lord, your word is a light to guide us. Help us to bring the light of Christ to everyone we meet.

SS842

LEADER:	(Turn off lights so that the only light comes from the Paschal candle.) Let us spend a few minutes thinking about how we can bring light, joy, and love to others. (Short pause.) Jesus teaches us that we are the light of the world and must live as children of the light. Every kind word or act we do makes the world a little brighter for others. Today each of you will receive a special way to bring the light of Christ to others this week.
	Play "You Are the Light of the World" from the GODSPELL album softly in the background. One at a time call each child to the front. Have the child use a long match to light his vigil light from the Paschal candle (or do it for him). Give the child an action card while saying,
LEADER:	(Name), live as a child of the light.
ALL:	(Except child receiving card) The Lord will shine upon you.
	When all the children have received their cards, sing "Candles on the Altar" (page 41).
CLOSING PRAYER:	Dear Jesus, we are special because you have made us children of light. Let your light shine in our hearts and chase away the darkness. Help us to follow you and be a light to one another. Amen.

LIGHT IN THE DARKNESS BARS

1 cup softened margarine
1 cup packed light brown sugar
2 large eggs
1 teaspoon vanilla

2 cups flour
1 teaspoon baking powder
1 cup chocolate chips
Chocolate frosting

Grease and flour a 9" x 13" pan. Melt the chocolate chips over low heat, stirring often. Cool. Beat sugar and margarine until fluffy. Add vanilla and eggs. Beat well. Stir in baking powder and flour until well blended. Transfer half the batter to another bowl. Stir the melted chocolate chips into the remaining batter. Spread the chocolate batter in the pan. Top with light batter. Bake at 350° for 30 to 35 minutes. Cool in pan on a rack. When cool, add frosting. Cut into 24 bars.

Shining Star Publications, Copyright © 1987, A division of Good Apple, Inc.

SS842

CANDLES ON THE ALTAR
Words and Music by Helen Kitchell Evans
Frances M. Benson

1. Can-dles burn-ing bright-ly are so nice to see they make me think of Je-sus and his love for me.
2. Can-dles glow like sun-shine in the spring-time air Tell-ing me that Je-sus is — ev-ery-where;

Through the dark-ened win-dows I can see the light when I go to church at night_____
As the pret-ty can-dles burn I hear them say "Walk with dear Je-sus each day

Chorus

Can-dles on the al-tar bright-ly shine, bright-ly shine, Tell-ing me that Je-sus is a friend of mine, friend of mine

Light-ing up the dark-ness Giv-ing out a glow Tell-ing me he loves me so.

SS842

ACTION CARDS

No one, when he has lit a lamp, covers it . . . or puts it under a bed, but sets it on a lampstand, that those who enter may see the light.   Luke 8:16

Share one of your special talents to help a classmate this week.

"Let your light so shine before men, that they may see your good works and glorify your Father in heaven."   Matthew 5:16

Do something this week to show others how to be kind to other children.

"While you have the light, believe in the light, that you may become sons of light . . . ."   John 12:36

Do something this week to cheer up a classmate who is unhappy or feels bad about something.

"As long as I am in the world, I am the light of the world."   John 9:5

Do something to make the world a happier place for your family and classmates this week.

He who loves his brother abides in the light . . . .   I John 2:10

Do something this week to show another person that you love him.

The Lord is my light and my salvation; whom shall I fear? The Lord is the strength of my life . . . .   Psalm 27:1

Share your thoughts about God with a classmate to help make his faith stronger.

Then God said, "Let there be light"; and there was light. And God saw the light, that it was good . . . .   Genesis 1:3,4

Help others see something good about a thing that God created that children don't usually like.

. . . Walk as children of light . . . in all goodness, righteousness, and truth . . . .   Ephesians 5:8,9

Do something this week to change something that is wrong.

In Him was life, and the life was the light of men. And the light shines in the darkness . . . .   John 1:4,5

Bring light into a classmate's life by being kind or paying him a compliment.

". . . If anyone walks in the day, he does not stumble, because he sees the light of the world. But if one walks in the night, he stumbles, because the light is not in him."   John 11:9,10

Find something good about someone you don't like very much.

Duplicate enough cards for each child in class. Fold each card in half, printing inside, and attach a candle sticker to the front.

Shining Star Publications, Copyright © 1987, A division of Good Apple, Inc.

SS842

THE WHEAT, THE VINE AND THE FIG TREE

And He spoke to them a parable: "Look at the fig tree, and all the trees. When they are already budding, you see and know . . . that summer is now near. So you, likewise, when you see these things happening, know that the kingdom of God is near. Assuredly, I say to you, this generation will by no means pass away till all things are fulfilled. Heaven and earth will pass away, but My words will by no means pass away."

Luke 21:29-33

The Palestine of Jesus' time was primarily an agricultural country. The people either kept flocks on the hillsides or worked the fields, vineyards or fruit groves. The Israelites cultivated forms of the natural vegetation. It was their way to grow wheat, vines, and olive trees together, and they seldom settled in an area where these three could not be raised together on the same farm, although crop concentrations varied from region to region. The fig tree was also a commonly cultivated crop in some areas. Because of this, many of Jesus' parables dealt with plants and agricultural practices that were part of the familiar life of the countryside.

SS842

THE PARABLE OF A SEED

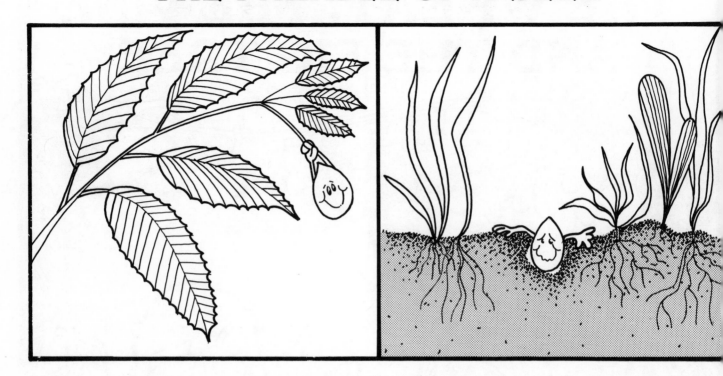

Once upon a time there was a seed so small you could hardly see it, so very small it could amost slip between your fingers.

One day while the little seed was singing and swinging back and forth on the top branch of a beautiful tree, she heard her tree boasting to another.

"Do you know that once I was a little seed? Now look at me—I am the biggest and most beautiful tree in the yard."

And all at once, our little seed knew deep inside her that what she wanted most of all was to be a big beautiful tree.

But how?
How could she ever do this?

The little seed was about to ask the beautiful tree, when suddenly. . . .

A strange wind blew her right off the tree and carried her far away . . . and finally dropped her on the ground.

The little seed looked all around her . . . She was alone . . . She was frightened . . . And she cried because she did not know how to become a tree. And she wanted this with all her heart.

As the days went on, she found herself slipping into the soil. It was dark . . . It was cold . . . It was lonesome . . . "I will never be a tree!" she cried.

After a long time it got very cold, but the little seed did not worry too much, because she had a warm coat.

But then it happened! It got so very, very cold, and one day the little seed heard a strange sound. It was a crack in her coat, her beautiful coat that always protected her.

She felt so weak, so miserable. "I will die for sure now!" she thought.

But then she felt something seeping through the crack; it was water, and she drank and drank, because she was so thirsty.

As she drank, she felt herself growing stronger until she pushed against her coat and cracked it wide open.

It was a strange feeling to be without her coat that always protected her.

She reached deep into the soil and found more water to drink. Then feeling very strong, she pushed up through the soil until at long last she saw LIGHT!

Shining Star Publications, Copyright © 1987, A division of Good Apple, Inc.

SS842

And the light warmed her. She drank more water from the soil and grew and grew and grew. She could hardly recognize herself anymore. The little seed thanked the soil and the water and the sun for helping her.

Many years passed, and the little seed became a beautiful tree, with leaves and flowers and her own seeds.

One day she looked at her tiny seeds singing and swinging on her top branches, and she said, "Oh little seeds, someday you can be beautiful trees, too. But before that happens you must let yourselves be blown by the wind, covered by the soil, frozen, and cracked wide open.

You will have to leave the safe places inside your coats. You will have to let the water and the sun help you, and most of all, you will have to wait . . . and wait . . . and wait . . .!

But it will happen! You will grow! You will become beautiful trees and you will make many people happy because you are so beautiful."

DISCUSSION QUESTIONS

1. If Jesus came to Earth today, He might tell a parable like this one. What lesson do you think this little story teaches?

2. What did the little seed want most of all?

3. Why was the little seed so frightened?

4. Can you think of a time when you were scared and lost like the little seed?

5. Why did the little seed think she would never become a tree?

6. Why did the little seed think she would die?

7. How did the water and the light help the little seed?

8. What did the tree mean when she told the little seeds that they would have to leave their safe places if they wanted to become trees?

9. What will you have to do if you want to grow up? Will it be easy?

10. "He who loses his life will find it." What do you think this means? Do you think the little seed found this to be true?

SS842

THE FRUITFUL GRAIN OF WHEAT

"... unless a grain of wheat falls into the ground and dies, it remains alone; but if it dies, it produces much grain."

John 12:24

Ask the children to suggest some ways that this verse is like the story of the little seed. Before He died, Jesus told His friends that He was something like a seed or grain of wheat. Like the grain of wheat and the little seed in the story, Jesus had to die and be buried before He could rise again and bring us new life.

PLANT SOME SEEDS

Bring in a wheat-growing kit (sold in pet stores; contains a special soil and wheat seed to grow greens for cats) or a pack of marigold seeds and some potting soil. Talk about the fact that the seeds won't grow until they are buried under the soil. Let each child plant a seed in a section of a styrofoam egg carton. Place some seeds between layers of wet paper towels. Keep the towels moist. Let the children check every other day or so to see what is happening to the seeds. The seeds placed between the towel layers will sprout. These can then be transferred to soil for growing. Have them check their planted seeds regularly for signs of growth.

A peanut is a kind of seed. Split open a peanut so the children can see the tiny plant (embryo) inside the seed. Explain that the embryo is the beginning of a tiny plant inside every seed. Help the children understand the growing process by asking questions such as

> What happens to a seed that just lies on top of the soil? (It rots or the wind blows it away.)
> What does the seed need to make it grow? (It needs water, sunlight, nutrients from the soil.)
> What happens to the seed when it is planted? (It begins to sprout.)
> What happens to the rest of the seed when the tiny plant has sprouted? (The sprout uses up the rest of the seed for food, and the seed disappears or dies.)

Use pictures to show the children the various stages of wheat growth. Point out how the tiny seed eventually produces a stalk of wheat that contains many grains of wheat (seeds), each of which can become a whole new plant.

SS842

JESUS AND THE WHEAT

Show the children a stalk of wheat. Ask them why Jesus compared Himself to a grain of wheat. Discuss the fact that as the wheat seed dies, it becomes a new form of life. When Jesus died, He rose from the dead just like a new green plant comes from the seed when it dies. Through His death, Jesus won for us a new life. He died so that we could share in His harvest of salvation.

Point out that the stalk of wheat has many grains. Each of these will eventually grow into a new wheat plant. The wheat seed died so that it could produce many grains of wheat. Jesus died so that He could give us a new life with God.

THE WHEAT AND THE WEEDS

Jesus told another story about wheat to teach us a lesson about people. Some words are missing in the poem below. Choose the right words from the box and print them on the lines in the poem.

One day a farmer planted his field
with the best wheat _____ around.
That night his enemy came and
Planted weeds in that very same _____.

The summer _____ warmed the soil,
And the gentle rain watered the seeds.
The farmer's wheat grew green and strong,
And so did his enemy's _____

"Should we pull the weeds?" the servants asked.
"No," said the farmer with a weary sigh.
"Let the _____ and weeds grow side by side.
If you pull the weeds, some wheat might _____."

When harvest time came, the farmer said,
"Now pull the weeds and _____ them all.
Then gather the wheat into my barn,
For my crop has grown strong and _____."

Some people are like weeds that
Grow in the field of the _____,
but you will be God's golden wheat
If you grow in _____ and keep His word.

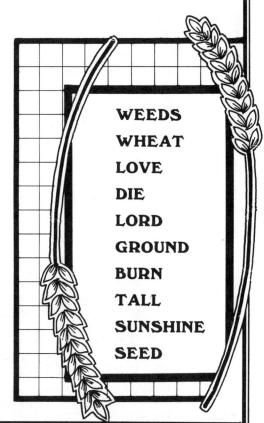

WEEDS

WHEAT

LOVE

DIE

LORD

GROUND

BURN

TALL

SUNSHINE

SEED

Based on Matthew 13:24-30

SS842

THE VINE AND THE BRANCHES

One day Jesus told the Disciples that He is like the grapevine and the people who believe in Him are like the branches. Jesus said, ''. . . As the branch cannot bear fruit of itself, unless it abides in the vine, neither can you, unless you abide in Me. I am the vine, you are the branches. He who abides in Me, and I in him, bears much fruit; for without Me you can do nothing.''

John 15:4,5

The cultivation of grapes and the care of the vineyard was a chief occupation of the Jewish people, so the Disciples were able to understand Jesus' message. To help the children understand what Jesus was saying, display pictures of vineyards, vines and grapes. Talk about the fact that the branches of the grapevine depend on the vine for the things they need to produce good fruit. The vine gives the branches the water and nutrients from the soil they need to grow. Like the vine, Jesus gives us His love. He teaches us how to be kind and loving to others. If we love one another, we bear much fruit.

Cut off a branch or a leaf from a plant and let the children observe what happens to it over the course of a few days. Discuss what happens when we cut ourselves off from Jesus and from one another.

GRAPEVINE BULLETIN BOARD

Cover the bulletin board with white paper. Add a drawing of a large grapevine to illustrate the verse from John 15:4,5. Give each child a ''grape'' cut from colored paper. (Grapes come in a variety of colors—black, blue, golden, green, purple, red and white—just as our actions vary.) Have each child put loving words or a picture of someone doing an act of love on a grape and add it to the cluster of grapes on the board. The fruit we bear is the happiness our loving words and actions bring to others.

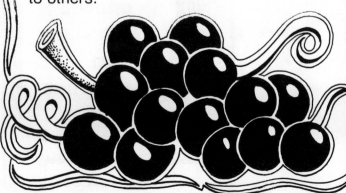

JESUS IS THE VINE. WE ARE THE BRANCHES.

SS842

THE PARABLE OF THE BARREN FIG TREE

The fig tree was the first plant named in Genesis and was a favorite among biblical people. Because it was so familiar to His followers, Jesus often chose the fig tree as a way of teaching lessons in His parables. Share this story based on Luke 13:6-9.

Once, long ago when Jesus lived, there was a man who had a grove of fig trees growing in his vineyard. All the trees were tall and green and full of fruit—all, that is, except one little tree. The little fig tree was not beautiful like the others. He was short and scraggly. His branches were thin and bare, and no figs grew on them. Each day the little fig tree stood in the shadows of the other fig trees and wished he could be more like them.

One day the owner of the vineyard and the gardener came into the fig grove. They stopped and looked at each tree. The owner smiled happily at each tree and praised it for its beautiful fruit. The little fig tree was nervous. He hoped the owner wouldn't notice how thin and scraggly he was.

When the two men approached the little fig tree, the owner became very angry. "Look," he said to the gardener, "for three years I have been coming here looking for figs on this fig tree, and I haven't found any. Cut it down! Why should it go on using up the soil?"

The poor little fig tree was very frightened. His bare little branches shook with fear. He didn't want to be cut down, but he knew the owner was right. "If only I had a single fig among my branches," the little tree thought sadly, "maybe the owner would let me live."

Now the gardener was a kind, gentle man, and he felt sorry for the little fig tree. "Please, sir," he said to the owner. "Leave it alone for just one more year. I will dig around it and put in some fertilizer. Then if the tree bears figs next year, so much the better; if not, then you can cut it down."

So all year the gardener worked with the little fig tree. Under the gardener's loving care, the little fig tree grew green and full. When the owner came to the grove again, he was amazed to find the finest figs he had ever seen.

Cut the figures below from lightweight tagboard. Cut several fruitful fig trees. Color the figures. Glue each to a band of paper cut to fit the child's finger. Children use the finger puppets to act out the story while you read it.

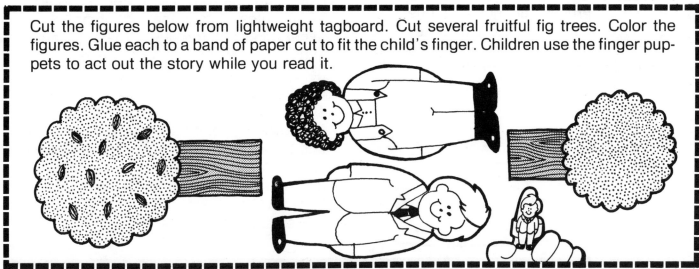

SS842

LESSONS FROM THE FIG TREES

JESUS, THE GARDENER

Jesus is like the gardener in the story of the little fig tree. He wants us to grow up strong and healthy and produce much fruit. Even when it seems that we are not at all what He wants us to be, Jesus does not give up on us. He is gentle and patient and helps us to grow in love and faith so that we can be good Christians. Ask the children to suggest some ways that Jesus is like the gardener in this story and like the vinedresser in John 15:1,2.

THE CURSED FIG TREE

Read Matthew 21:18,19. In this passage Jesus is angry when He finds no figs on the tree and says it will never produce fruit. At first this passage seems to be the opposite of Luke 13:6-9. Jesus is not patient and gentle with this fig tree. Explain to the children that a fig tree usually bears fruit before it grows leaves. When Jesus saw a fig tree with a lot of leaves on it, He expected to find some ripe, juicy figs hidden among the leaves. He was disappointed because He found no fruit, only a big show of leaves. Ask the children to suggest some ways that people are sometimes like this tree.

"... A TREE IS KNOWN BY ITS FRUIT."
Matthew 12:33

Jesus teaches us that people will know we are His followers by our "fruits." Draw a big tree. Cut fruit shapes from colored paper. Read Galatians 5:22,23 to find the fruits of the Spirit. Print each on a fruit shape. Then draw a picture that shows how you can demonstrate each fruit in your own life. Glue the fruits to your tree. Print your name on the trunk. Print this verse on your picture: "You will know them by their fruits . . . ."   Matthew 7:16

FIG COOKIES

Since the fig tree produced both a summer and a winter crop, there was never a shortage of figs in Palestine. For the Israelites, the fig tree was a symbol of plenty, peace and serenity (see Micah 4:3,4.) It was their custom to present an honored guest or visitor with a basket of figs or fig cakes. The children might enjoy making fig cookies and sharing them with another class. To save time, prepare the figs in advance.

½ pound dried figs
½ cup butter
¾ cup sugar
2 eggs
½ cup honey
2¾ cups flour
½ cup chopped nuts

3 teaspoons baking powder
½ teaspoon salt
2 tablespoons fruit juice (water from cooking figs)

Cover the figs with cold water and simmer 10 minutes. Drain (saving some of the juice) and chop the figs. Cream the butter and sugar together. Add the eggs and honey, beating well. Mix the dry ingredients together, and gradually add to the butter-sugar mixture until well-blended. Stir in the fruit juice, figs and nuts. Drop by teaspoonfuls two-inches apart on a greased cookie sheet. Bake for 6 to 8 minutes at 375° or until done. Cool slightly before removing from sheet.

Makes about four dozen cookies.

SS842

THE FIG TREE

Jesus cursed the fig tree because it did not produce fruit, even though it had already sent forth its leaves. Without fruit, the fig tree could not bring forth new life. As you sing this song, think about some of the ways Jesus wants you to bear fruit in your life.

THE FIG TREE

Words and Music by Helen Kitchell Evans
Frances Mann Benson

When Jesus came to a fig tree He found the tree was bare. No fruit was growing upon it So Jesus said right there: "Oh, fig tree, Oh fig tree, Only leaves I see today. Because you have no fruit today, You will just wither away."

(gradually slower and softer)

SS842

NEW LIFE CRAFTS

FLOWERING FIG TREE

A tree blossoming in spring is a sign of new life, a sign of summer after the darkness of winter. During His last week, Jesus used the flowering fig tree as a symbol to explain the coming of the kingdom of God. The children might enjoy making a flowering tree of their own to remind them that Jesus died so that we might have eternal life and inherit the kingdom of God.

Find a tree branch you like. Plug the hole in the bottom of a flowerpot with clay. Fill the pot with plaster of paris. Insert the branch when the plaster begins to harden. Cut leaves from green construction paper and glue them to the branch. Add paper flowers made from two-inch squares of tissue paper. To make the flowers, place the eraser end of a pencil in the center of a tissue square. Gather the sides up around the pencil as shown. Dip the flower into a bit of glue, attach it to the branch, and then remove the pencil. Glue an appropriate verse to the flowerpot if desired.

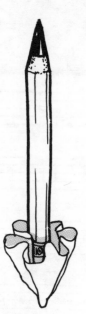

3-D FRUIT PLACARD

"...HE WHO ABIDES IN ME ... BEARS MUCH FRUIT ...."
John 15:5

The fruit of plants like the wheat, the grapevine, and the fig tree contain all that is needed to produce a new plant. When we bring Christ's love to others, we too bear fruit which gives new life. Make a large drawing, like the one on the left, on white tagboard. Using yarn and glue, fill in the wheat stalks and figs; add puffed wheat cereal to the wheat stalks and colored glass or plastic bits to the grapes. Glue on some fabric leaves and a twig stem for the bunch of grapes. Add an appropriate Bible verse.

SS842

THE LORD'S SUPPER

Now on the first day of the Feast of the Unleavened Bread the disciples came to Jesus, saying to Him, ''Where do You want us to prepare for You to eat the Passover?'' And He said, ''Go into the city to a certain man, and say to him, 'The Teacher says, ''My time is at hand; I will keep the Passover at your house with My disciples.'' ' ''

. . . Now when evening had come, He sat down with the twelve . . . And as they were eating, Jesus took bread, blessed it and broke it, and gave it to the disciples and said, ''Take, eat; this is My body.'' Then He took the cup, and gave thanks, and gave it to them, saying, ''Drink from it all of you. For this is My blood of the new convenant, which is shed for many for the remission of sins.''   Matthew 26:17,18,20, 26-28

When Jesus chose to make bread the symbol of Himself at the Last Supper, he was using a word that everyone was familiar with, for bread was the staple food of every home. Bread was also an important religious symbol in the Temple. Every Sabbath, twelve freshly baked loaves of bread were placed on a table of gold in the holy place of the Tabernacle. Known as *showbread*, it was the bread of ''the presence of God.'' The showbread was a reminder to the Israelites of how God had provided for them in the wilderness and a sign of God's goodness and provision for all time.

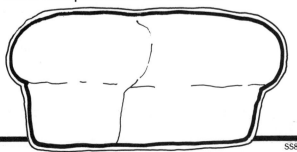

SS842

BREAD—SYMBOL OF JESUS

At the Last Supper, Jesus made bread the symbol of Himself when He took bread, broke it, and gave it to His Disciples, saying, "This is my body." The choice of bread as a symbol was an appropriate one. Bread was closely associated with Jesus from the time of His birth.

Read Matthew 2:1 to find the name of the town where Jesus was born. Print it on the line.

— — — — — — — — — —

Start at the left side of the puzzle below and cross out the letters that spell the name of this town. The twelve letters you did not cross out will spell the meaning of the town's name. Print the letters on the lines below the puzzle.

B H O E U S T E H O L F B R E E H E A M D

— — — — — — — — — — — —

MAKE A MURAL

Organize the children into groups. Ask each group to find a different passage in the Bible where bread is associated with Jesus, or assign each group one of the passages below. Ask each group to illustrate its event on a large sheet of poster paper as part of a mural. As a class, discuss the events depicted in the mural. Possible passages include
  Feeding the five thousand - Mark 6:30-44
  Feeding the four thousand - Mark 8:1-10
  The Lord's Prayer - Matthew 6:9-13
  The temptation to turn stones into bread - Matthew 4:1-4
  Jesus warns the Disciples against the Pharisees and the Sadducees
                                                    Matthew 16:5-12
  The Last Supper - Matthew 26:26-30
  Sharing a meal with the Disciples in Emmaus after the Resurrection
                                                    Luke 24:28-35
  Sharing a meal with the seven Disciples after the Resurrection
                                                    John 21:11-13
  Jesus the bread of life - John 6:25-40; 41-58.

BREAKING BREAD

In Jesus' time bread was made daily in the shape of round, flat loaves over the open fire. Bread was never cut but always broken by hand and given by the head of the household to the rest of the family or guests. Breaking bread was considered to be a token of hospitality. Jesus often broke bread with His Disciples. He spent His last night with His Disciples sharing the Passover meal, and He shared two meals with His friends after His Resurrection. But Jesus also broke bread with those who were not His close followers. Read one or more of the following passages in the Bible: Mark 2:13-17, Luke 7:36-50, Luke 19:1-10. How did others react when Jesus chose to share a meal with each of these people? What did Jesus' willingness to break bread with outcasts show us about Him?

PLAN A MENU

Luke 5:29 tells us that the tax collector Levi (Matthew) prepared a great feast for Jesus to which a number of tax collectors and others were invited. What do you suppose they had to eat? We know that bread was a staple food of every home and that it was an important part of the meal. (It was often used to scoop out hot food from a communal bowl.) Use a Bible encyclopedia to find out what kinds of food were eaten in Jesus' day. Then plan a menu for the feast that Levi prepared for Jesus.

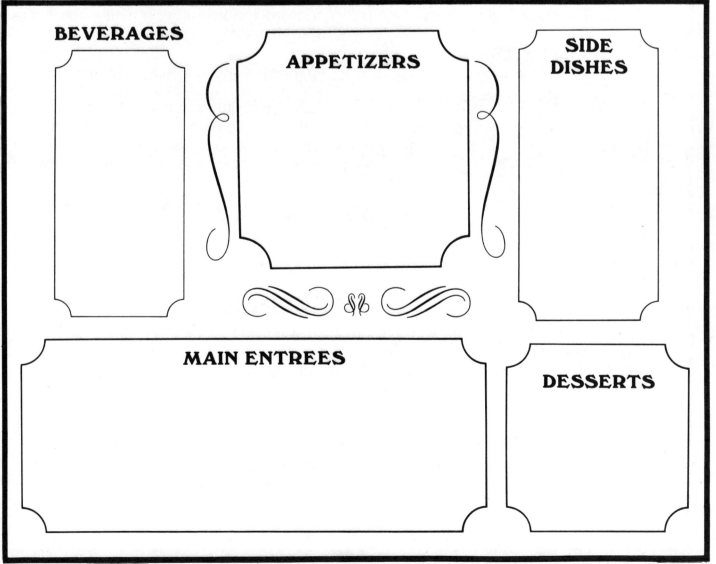

                    SS842

SHARING MEALS

Meals play an important part in our lives. Besides nourishment, they provide us with rest, company, and often happiness. Ask the children if they enjoy eating alone. How do they feel when they eat alone? (Often people eat faster when they are alone so they can get on to other activities; or they read a book or watch TV.)

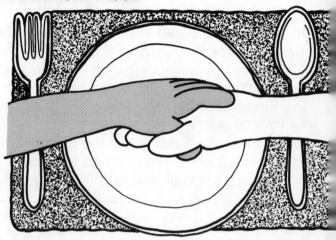

Discuss the importance of shared meals by asking such questions as

> How important are shared meals in our lives?
> For what reasons do we share meals with others?
> What are some special events in our lives that we celebrate by sharing meals with friends?
> What can we do to make the meals we share with others joyful events?

Set aside some time on a regular basis to share a meal with your students. Eating lunch with your students helps you to learn more about them as individuals and lets the children know you enjoy their company. You'll be surprised at how the children look forward to these special times you share with them.

Planning a potluck supper for the children and their families can be a good way to encourage children to think about the importance of sharing meals. Ask each family to bring a dish to share. The children can get ready for the special event by making decorations, designing invitations to their families, and planning some simple entertainment.

THE LAST SUPPER

Jesus invites us to share a meal with Him too. Ask the children when this meal takes place. The word communion means sharing and is most closely linked to the events of the Last Supper at which Jesus shared Himself with the Disciples and with us. Ask the children to suggest some reasons why Jesus chose to share Himself with us through a meal rather than in some other way.

Organize the children into groups of three or four. Give each group a songbook and have the children find songs that express the joy of meeting Jesus through communion. Ask each child to illustrate one or more parts of his song. Have each group share its illustrations and the song with the rest of the children.

SS842

THE STAFF OF LIFE

The word bread signifies the staff of life. Food is one of our most important daily needs. Without it, we would die. Grain, from which bread is made, is the single most important food item. Almost everyone in the world eats some kind of bread. Have the children think about how important bread is in our lives. As a class project, find pictures of the various foods we could not eat if there were no bread or grain products. Make a collage.

THE LIVING BREAD

Jesus said, ''. . . I am the bread of life. He who comes to Me shall never hunger . . . .'' John 6:35. Ask the children to suggest reasons why Jesus chose bread as a symbol for Himself. How would our lives be different without Jesus? How does He provide nourishment for us? How does He help us to grow? Have the children use an encyclopedia to find pictures of different kinds of bread. Then cut out bread shapes and on each write a way Jesus feeds our hunger. Make a display entitled ''Jesus—Bread of Life.''

ONE BREAD, ONE BODY

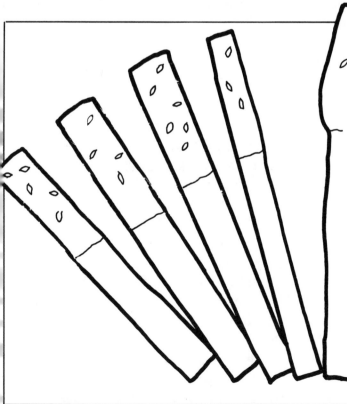

Paul tells us that although we are many, we are one bread, one body in Christ, because we all share one bread—Jesus. (I Corinthians 1:10-17) Use a loaf of bread as an analogy. Just as there are many slices of bread in the loaf, so there are many people who follow Jesus. All the slices together make up the loaf of bread, just as all Christians make up the body of Christ. Jesus lives in all of us, so we too are bread. Ask the children to suggest ways we, as Christians, feed the needs of each other.

SS842

PREPARATION FOR THE PASSOVER CELEBRATION

THE PASSOVER FOODS

You will need a small paper cup and plate for each guest. Place the following on each plate: parsley, horseradish, slice of hard-cooked egg and a dollop of haroset. Place plates of broken matzah and small bowls of saltwater within reach of each guest. Place a matzah wrapped in a napkin and a lamb (coconut-frosted cake in the shape of a lamb) in the center of the table. Extra matzah may be placed near the leader's place. Nonalcoholic wine or grape juice will also be needed.

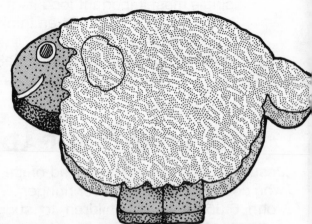

OTHER PREPARATION

Duplicate a copy of the script for each child. On the lines write the names of the children who will read each part. Assign the youngest child the parts marked CHILD. Allow time for the children to practice their parts and learn the song. Be sure to duplicate enough copies of the song for the children and guests.

Have several bowls of warm water and several cloths available. If there are quite a few guests, you may wish to have more than one section washing hands at the same time. Place a large candle in the center of the table. Try to seat everyone so that all can see and hear the leader and the children.

MATZAH BREAD

4 cups unbleached flour
1 teaspoon salt
1½ cups water (room temperature)

Combine the flour and salt. Add enough water to make a dough that can be formed into a ball and is not sticky. Place the dough on a floured surface and knead for 10 minutes. Shape into a ball and cut it in half. Cut each half into 8 pieces. Form 16 balls. Roll out each ball into a 7-inch circle. Place on an ungreased cookie sheet. Bake in a preheated oven at 500°F for 5 minutes or until the bread is lightly colored, crisp and blistered.

Pita Bread may be used in place of the matzah.

HAROSET

1½ cups chopped nuts
1½ cups diced apples (peeled)
3 teaspoons cinnamon
3 tablespoons sugar
Nonalcholic red wine as desired

The haroset may be mixed together as is, but a paste would be more appropriate. To make a paste, place all the ingredients in a blender. Use just enough wine to add moisture. Blend at a high speed, adding wine as needed. Store in a covered dish until ready to use. This recipe yields enough haroset for 12 to 18 people.

Shining Star Publications, Copyright © 1987, A division of Good Apple, Inc.

58

SS842

A PASSOVER CELEBRATION

LEADER: On the night before He died, Jesus and His Disciples celebrated the Passover at the home of a Jewish friend. Let us pretend that we are in that upper room. We have gathered together to celebrate the passover of God's people from slavery to freedom.

_____: At the Last Supper, Jesus washed the feet of His friends to show them how much He loved them. He calls us to serve each other out of love.

(Each person, in turn, washes the hands of the person to his left.)

ALL: Thank you, Lord, for showing us how to serve others.

LEADER: We pour the wine from one bowl to show that we are all one in God. (Pour wine into each person's cup.)

_____: At the Last Supper, Jesus gave wine to his friends and said, "Take this and drink it. I tell you that I will not drink of the fruit of the vine again until I drink it with you in my Father's kingdom."

ALL: (Drink the wine.)

_____: Each of the foods we will eat has a special meaning for the Jewish people. The youngest child always asks the questions at the Passover meal.

CHILD: Why do we dip the parsley in salt water?

_____: (lighting candle) We light this candle to remind us that God promised to send us a light in our darkness. Jesus is that light.

CHILD: Why is this day different from other days?

_____: This is the day of the Passover. Listen to this story.
(Read Exodus 12:1-14)

_____: When the Jews celebrated Passover long ago, they blessed their food before eating it. Like them, we ask for God's blessing on the food we eat.

ALL: (Have the children say a familiar before-meal grace.)

SS842

_____: The parsley reminds us that nature comes to life in springtime. The salt water reminds us of the tears and the sweat of the Jews who were slaves in Egypt.

ALL: (Dip the parsley in salt water and eat.)

CHILD: Why do we eat matzah?

_____: Matzah is bread that is made without yeast. Yeast makes bread rise, but it takes time. Because the Jews had to leave Egypt quickly, they did not have time to wait for the bread to rise.

LEADER: (Break the bread and give each child a piece.) We break one piece of bread for each person and pass it to everyone to show that we are one. A long time ago, the owner of the house gave a guest a piece of bread to show love.

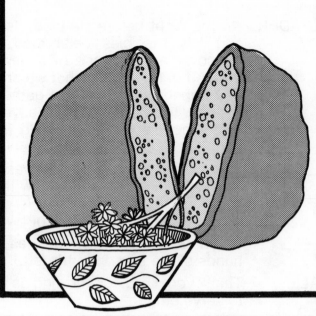

ALL: (Eat the bread.)

CHILD: Why do we eat bitter herbs?

_____: The bitter herbs remind us that the lives of the Jews were made bitter by slavery. They also remind us of Jesus' suffering and death.

ALL: (Eat the bitter herbs, horseradish)

CHILD: Why do we eat haroset?

_____: The haroset is a mixture of apples, spices, nuts and wine. It looks like the mortar the Jews used to build the Pharaoh's cities while they were slaves.

ALL: (Take a piece of matzah and scoop out some haroset. Eat it.)

CHILD: The Jews ate lamb at this meal. Why do we have a lamb on the table?

_____: God told the Jewish slaves to put the blood of a lamb on their doors so that the angel of death would pass over their houses and kill only the first born of the Egyptians. That night the Jews passed over into freedom.

_____: Jesus is called the Lamb of God because He died to give us eternal life.

CHILD: Why do we eat this egg?

_____: The egg is a sign of new growth, new hope and new life. Jesus gave us new life when He died for us, just as God gave the Jews new life when he freed them from slavery in Egypt.

SS842

ALL: (Eat the egg.)

_____: (Unwrap the piece of matzah and give it to the leader.) It is the custom to end the Passover meal with this matzah.

LEADER: (Break the matzah and pass it to all.) At the Last Supper, Jesus took the bread, broke it and gave it to His friends saying, ''Take and eat; this is my body which is to be given for you.''

ALL: (Eat the matzah.)

LEADER: (Pour wine into each person's cup.) After he had eaten, Jesus took a cup of wine and offered thanks. Then He gave it to his friends and said, ''This is my blood which will be shed for the forgiveness of sins.''

ALL: (Drink the wine.)

CHILD: What is the New Passover?

_____: The New Passover is Easter. Jesus passed over from death to life. Let us end this celebration with a song.

ALL: (Sing the song.)

THE FOLLOWING SIMPLIFIED VERSION OF EXODUS 12:1-8, 11-14 MAY BE USED IN PLACE OF THE BIBLE PASSAGE.

At this time Moses and the people of Israel were slaves in Egypt. The Lord spoke to Moses and said:

On the fourteenth of the month, at night, your people are to kill and eat a lamb. The people are to put some of the blood on the doors of their houses. You must eat the lamb quickly and be dressed to travel. It is the Passover Festival to honor me, your God.

On that night I will go through the land of Egypt, killing every firstborn. When I see the blood of the lamb on a door, I will pass over you and not harm you when I punish the Egyptians.

Keep holy this Passover Festival day and celebrate it forever, because it is on this day that I will bring the people of Israel out of slavery and punish the Egyptians.

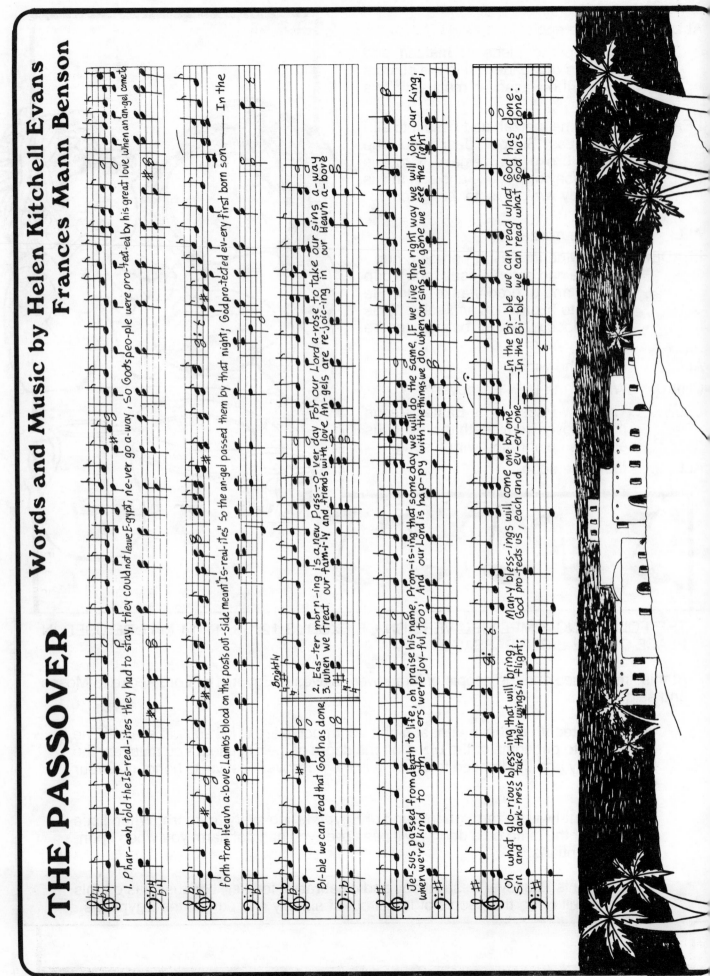

THE PASSOVER

Words and Music by Helen Kitchell Evans
Frances Mann Benson

SS842

BREAD CRAFTS

BREAD OF LIFE PLAQUE

For each plaque you will need a slice of cocktail rye bread, French bread or other small, solid type of bread. Choose an appropriate Bible verse about bread, such as John 6:33, John 6:35, John 6:51, or Matthew 6:11. Use alphabet macaroni to spell out the verse. Paint the letters and glue the macaroni onto the bread, spelling out the Bible verse. Glue a pop-top tab to the back of the bread, letting it extend over the top edge as a hanger. Varnish both sides of the bread. Add a bow and strawflowers or other decorations, as desired.

A GIFT OF BREAD

In Jesus' time the head of the household always offered bread to his guests as a sign of hospitality. Children might enjoy presenting someone they know with a gift of bread. A loaf of bread wrapped in a napkin and placed in a small basket is a nice gift for almost anyone. Have each child bring in a small basket or use plastic berry baskets. Each child should also have a white cloth napkin large enough to line the basket and cover the bread. Use thread or liquid embroidery paint to print the following saying on the part of the napkin that will cover the bread:

> Bread shared with friends
> makes every meal a feast.

Frozen bread dough, divided in thirds, can be baked in small loaf pans. Another possibility is to bake a boxed quick bread in small juice cans.

Bread Shared with Friends Makes Every Meal a Feast.

Shining Star Publications, Copyright © 1987, A division of Good Apple, Inc.

SS842

THE UPPER ROOM

In a Jewish home, the upper room was usually the guest room. It was often spacious and well-furnished. Jesus celebrated the Last Supper in such a room. Children might enjoy creating a Jewish home such as that in which Jesus' friend lived. Cut a door and window in two different size boxes. Attach the smaller box to the top of the larger box to form the upper room. Add a cardboard stairway or a ladder.

Jewish homes were usually made of clay and resembled stucco. To make "stucco" for your house, mix equal amounts (one cup of each) of flour and salt with just enough water to make a creamy, plaster-like mixture. Mix in a bit of brown tempera paint to make the stucco tan or brown. Spread the stucco over the outer walls of the house with a butter knife. When the stucco is dry, give the house a coat of shellac or clear varnish.

BREAD CLAY FIGURES

Make bread-dough clay for the entire class by increasing the recipe below or let each child make his own clay. To make the clay, remove the crust from a slice of white bread and tear the bread into small pieces. Add one tablespoon white glue to the bread, and knead it for five minutes until the dough is pliable and no longer sticky. Knead paste food coloring into the dough. Keep the dough in a plastic bag when you're not using it.

To make any shape, first roll the clay into a ball, then mold it into the desired shape. Pieces can be glued together with a dab of water. Allow the clay figure to air-dry on aluminum foil for about one week or until completely dry. Remove from the foil and coat with clear varnish or shellac. Children can use the clay to make chalices and bread or other Easter symbols and figures.

BREAD CLAY PLAQUES

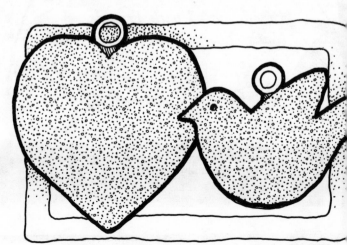

Make bread clay as above but without color. Roll the clay to one-half inch thickness. Cut out a desired shape with a cookie cutter. When the clay has dried, paint a favorite Bible verse on the plaque. Decorate as desired. Then give it a coat of clear varnish or shellac. Glue a pop-top tab to the back of the plaque as a hanger.

SS842

THE NEW COMMANDMENT

Jesus said . . . "Little children, I shall be with you a little while longer. You will seek Me; and as I said to the Jews, 'Where I am going, you cannot come,' so now I say to you. A new commandment I give to you, that you love one another; as I have loved you, that you also love one another. By this all will know that you are My disciples, if you have love for one another."

John 13:33-35

The Thursday before Easter is often called Maundy Thursday. The word comes from the Latin *mandatum* meaning "commandment," and refers to Jesus' new commandment to love one another, a commandment He issued at the Last Supper.

FLANNEL BOARD STORY
THE LOST SHEEP

Jesus told the parable of the lost sheep to show how much He cares for everyone, even those who may not love Him back. (Each time the word *cutout* is used, place the appropriate cutout on the flannel board.)

Once upon a time, long ago in the land of Perea, there lived a shepherd (cutout) who had many sheep. The shepherd loved all of his sheep very much and took very good care of them.

One day the shepherd gathered all his sheep (cutout—more than one may be used) together in the sheepfold. As he did every day, the shepherd counted his sheep to be sure all were there. But on this day, one lamb was missing. The shepherd was very worried. He knew he had to find the poor lost lamb before something happened to it. (Move cutout.)

The shepherd made sure that all the other sheep were safe in the fold. Then he picked up his staff and began to search the countryside for the lost lamb. The shepherd searched everywhere and called out to the lamb. He looked in the gullies. He looked among the rocks. He climbed up and down the hillside. But he could not find the little lost lamb. The shepherd grew very tired, but he did not give up his search. (Keep moving cutout.)

The shepherd was very worried. He had searched for many hours, but there was no sign of the lost lamb. The sun was settling lower in the sky, and the shepherd knew that it would soon be night. Suddenly, he heard a meek "baa". It seemed to be coming from a bush (cutout) farther up the hillside.

The shepherd rushed up the hill. There was the little lost lamb tangled up in a bush. The shepherd freed the lamb (cutout) and placed it upon his shoulders. Then he headed back to the flock (move cutout), singing and praising God as he went. His little lost lamb was home once more.

Based on Matthew 18:10-13

The shepherd led his sheep to pasture, remembered each one, and watched over them day and night. Jesus said He is like a shepherd who takes care of His sheep. Can you guess who the sheep are? Lead children to the realization that they are the sheep.

SHEPHERD

BUSH

SHEEP

LAMB

SS842

LITTLE LAMB PENDANTS

In some countries it is an Easter custom to wear gold or silver lambs on chains as charms. Children can make their own lamb pendants to wear as signs that they are Jesus' little lambs. To make lambs that are about one-half inch in size, use the pattern provided. (The finished charms will be about one-fourth the size of the pattern used.) Trace the pattern on clean foam meat trays. Cut out the lambs. Use a paper punch to punch out holes for the chains. (The holes will shrink too.) Place the lambs on a cookie sheet which has been lined with aluminum foil. Bake in the oven at 275 degrees for one and one-half minutes. The foam lambs will swell up at first and then shrink. Remove the pan from the oven and allow the lambs to cool. Attach each to a chain or a ribbon.

Read John 10:1-16. Talk about how the Good Shepherd treats the sheep differently than does the hired man. Jesus said that the hired man runs away when he sees the wolf coming because the sheep are not his, and he does not love them. Ask the children to describe what the Good Shepherd would do. Jesus said that He is the Good Shepherd. Talk about the ways in which Jesus is like a shepherd. Discuss how we, His sheep, know Him and will not follow another, and the ways in which Jesus leads us. Like the shepherd, He gives His life for us because we are truly His and He loves us.

JESUS—THE GOOD SHEPHERD

The image of the shepherd devoted to the care of his flock is an important one in the Bible. God Himself is often referred to as the Shepherd of Israel. Jesus called Himself the Good Shepherd who was ready to lay down His life for His sheep. Assign a research project in which the children find out all they can about how sheep behave, and how a shepherd cares for his flock. Older students or parents could help younger children find the information in library books and encyclopedias.

SS842

GOOD SHEPHERD MOBILE

Jesus said, "My sheep hear My voice, and I know them, and they follow Me. And I give them eternal life, and they shall never perish; neither shall anyone snatch them out of My hand." (John 10:27,28) The fourth Sunday of Easter is known as Good Shepherd Sunday. Have the children think about the ways Jesus calls us to follow Him, especially the ways we are to bring His love to others.

Enlarge the lamb's head pattern at the right and duplicate it on heavy paper or tagboard. Give each child a lamb. On the lamb's collar, the child can print his name. On the back of the lamb, have the child print a way he can show that he is Jesus' lamb. Arrange the lambs into a mobile with a cutout of Jesus as the Good Shepherd in a central position.

Print a name or a verse, such as Luke 15:6, on the base. Extend the base two inches on both sides. Staple the ends together in back to form a circular base.

GOOD SHEPHERD SEARCH

The Good Shepherd looks for His sheep everywhere, no matter what the risk to Himself. As followers of Jesus, the Good Shepherd, we too must search for His sheep. Ask the children to think about persons or groups of people in their homes, schools or neighborhoods who are sometimes forgotten, ignored or made fun of. How can they reach out to such people and welcome them into the fold by showing them Jesus' love?

The stand-up sheep at the left could be used to encourage the children to search out Jesus' lost lambs. Let each child make a lamb with his name on it. Stand the sheep on a table. Provide a supply of sheep with the words of Luke 15:6 written on each. Explain that each time a child demonstrates love for a "lost sheep," he may add (secretly if he wishes) another lamb to the fold. Caution the children to add a lamb only when they sincerely feel that they have reached out in love to someone they normally ignore or someone they don't get along with.

SS842

OUR LOVING SHEPHERD

Throughout the Gospels, Jesus compares His love for us to that of the shepherd for his sheep. As you sing this song, think about the ways that you can follow Jesus by showing others that you love them.

Words and Music by Kelly Riley
Frances Mann Benson

Gently and slowly

Je-sus is our lov-ing shep-herd. We are His lambs, faith-ful and true.
Like the shep-herd with all His lambs, He asks of you, "Come fol-low me."
Live like Je-sus ev-ery day, Lov- ing oth-ers as He loves you,

He watch-es o'er us with spe-cial care, And keeps us safe through the whole day long,
Show ev-ery one—— Christ's lov-ing ways. Be the friend He wants you al-ways to be.
Shar-ing His peace with all you meet, And fol-low-ing Him your whole life through.

SS842

THE LAMB OF GOD

He was oppressed and He was afflicted . . . He was led as a lamb to the slaughter, And as a sheep before its shearers is silent, So He opened not his mouth.   Isaiah 53:7

In the Hebrew religion, the life of a lamb was a sacrifice to God. Like that of the lamb, Jesus' life was sacrificed that we might have eternal life. When John, who was baptizing people at the river Jordan, saw Jesus coming toward him, he said, ''Behold! The Lamb of God who takes away the sins of the world!'' (John 1:29) John thought of Jesus as ''the Lamb'' who would sacrifice His life for the sake of those He loved. These words of John are frequently used in communion services. After His Crucifixion, Jesus was often referred to as ''the Lamb.'' The word ''Lamb'' is used to speak of Jesus throughout the Book of Revelation.

The ecclesiastical symbol of Easter is a lamb carrying a banner which bears a red cross. An appropriate art project for Easter would be a picture of this symbol which the children could display at home as a reminder that Jesus gave His life for them. Enlarge the lamb below and duplicate it on white tagboard. Have the children color the staff with a gold marker, outline the banner in blue, and color the lamb's face, ears and legs black. Add a red felt cross to the banner and pieces of cotton balls to the lamb's body to give it a fluffy look. Add a pop-top hanger to the back of the tagboard.

SS842

THEY'LL KNOW WE ARE CHRISTIANS

A Christian is a friend of Jesus. How will people be able to tell if you are a Christian? Jesus told His Disciples that there is a very special way to tell if you are Jesus' friend. Print the first letter of each picture on the space above it. Then you will know what Jesus told His friends.

Based on John 13:35

(Answers are found on page 144.)

Shining Star Publications, Copyright © 1987, A division of Good Apple, Inc. SS842

CALLED TO BE SHEPHERDS

After His Resurrection, when Jesus appeared to the Apostles, He asked Peter three times, ''Do you love Me?'' Each time, when Peter replied, ''Yes, Lord; You know that I love You,'' Jesus gave him a different command. The first time Jesus said, ''Feed My lambs.'' The second time He said, ''Tend My sheep,'' and the third time He said ''Feed My sheep.'' (Based on John 21:15-17) Jesus gives us the same commands. We, too, are called to be shepherds. We do this by loving one another as Jesus loved us.

LOVE SIGNS

What does it mean to love others as Jesus loves us? Ask the children to explain in their own words what this new commandment means to them. Then give each child a sheet of paper on which is printed, ''If I really love others as Jesus loves me, I will . . . .'' Ask each child to complete the statement and decorate his paper in some way. Display the signs around the room. On occasion, choose a sign and discuss its meaning.

LOVING LAMB PUZZLE

Another possibility is to make a loving lamb bulletin board. Place a cutout of Jesus (Good Shepherd) on the bulletin board, along with a caption reading ''Jesus is My Shepherd.'' Enlarge the lamb pattern on white tagboard. Cut into puzzle pieces. On each piece print, ''Because Jesus loves me, I . . . .'' Give each child a puzzle piece on which he completes the statement and signs his name. When the children have finished their pieces, let them reassemble the puzzle on the bulletin board.

RULES FOR SHEPHERDS

Like shepherds, we have rules to live by. Our rules are the Ten Commandments. Jesus tells us that all of these can be summed up in just two commandments: love God and love your neighbor. Read Matthew 22:37-39. As a class, discuss how each of the Ten Commandments really tells us ways to show our love for God and for others. Relate these two examples to the children's lives to help them better understand these commands.

Shining Star Publications, Copyright © 1987, A division of Good Apple, Inc.

SS842

MY SHEPHERD, MY FRIEND

John tells us that ''God is love.'' (I John 4:8) In his Gospel, John teaches us that if we want to know what God's love is like, we should look at the total giving involved in Jesus' love for us:''Greater love has no one than this, than to lay down one's life for his friends.'' (John 15:13) Jesus taught us what love and friendship mean by His own example. He was the kind of friend everyone would like to have. He was kind, giving, compassionate, unselfish, and loving—just like the shepherd with his flock.

GREATER LOVE HATH NO MAN
Words and Music by Kathy Jones

SS842

"LOVE" TREASURE HUNT

The commandment to love is the basis for Christian behavior. The noun *love* (agape) is used 117 times in the New Testament. The verb *to love* (agapan) appears 141 times, and the adjective *beloved* (agapetos) occurs 61 times. Altogether these three words are used over 300 times in the New Testament. Organize the children into teams and hold a "Love Treasure Hunt." Have each team search the New Testament for Scripture verses which speak of love. Which team can find the most? Talk about why love is mentioned so often.

A GOOD FRIEND IS . . .

Encourage the children to talk about friendships they have formed, and why they consider these people to be good friends. How do they know these people are their good friends? After the children have had an opportunity to share their feelings about friends, have the children brainstorm to make a list of the characteristics of good friends. Entitle the chart "A Good Friend Is . . ." and display it in the room for all to see.

LOVE YOUR ENEMY

Perhaps the most difficult part of Jesus' new commandment of love is for children to understand that it also means to love those people we don't like. In Matthew 5:44, Jesus said, "But I say to you, love your enemies, bless those who curse you, do good to those who hate you, and pray for those who spitefully use you and persecute you." The idea of loving your enemy can be hard for young children to comprehend. Talk about some situations where it is hard to love someone—when someone hits you, tattles on you in school, breaks your favorite toy on purpose. How do you feel at such times? What do you want to do? What do you think Jesus would do?

LOVE PUPPETS

Have the children bring in puppets from home, or make some simple puppets from old socks, yarn, buttons, and felt or fabric scraps. The puppets can be animals or people. Let the children work in groups of three or four to plan some simple puppet skits that show deeds of sharing, helping, and loving. Encourage the children to show ways of loving others in their puppet skits. You might want to provide the children with some suggestions, such as how to love a bully, a show-off, someone who is selfish or conceited. Encourage the children to think about what Jesus would want them to do in such cases, as they plan their skits. Share the skits with the class and talk about their messages.

SS842

GARDEN OF GETHSEMANE

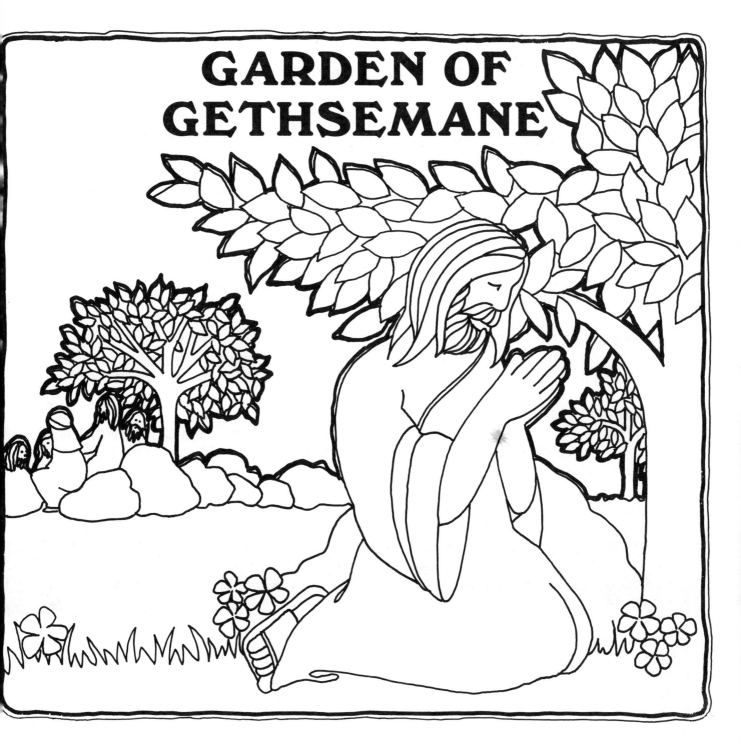

Then they came to a place which was named Gethsemane; and He said to His Disciples, "Sit here while I pray."

He went a little farther, and fell on the ground, and prayed that if it were possible, the hour might pass from Him.

And He said, "Abba, Father, all things are possible for You. Take this cup away from Me; nevertheless, not what I will, but what You will."   Mark 14:32,35,36

The Garden of Gethsemane is located just east of Jerusalem, across the Kidron, on the side of the Mount of Olives. Jesus went there often to pray.

Jesus taught His followers to come to God as children to a loving and forgiving Father. He taught them to address God personally and to ask Him and trust Him to provide their needs, but He also taught them, by His own example, to accept God's will.

JESUS PRAYS IN THE GARDEN

In the garden Jesus prayed for Himself, for His Disciples, and for all who would believe in Him in the future. Jesus' prayers, particularly those in John, are difficult for children to understand. Ask the children what they think Jesus said in His prayer for Himself. Then read certain verses from a GOOD NEWS or other simplified Bible to the children, and talk about the main points of the prayer. Do the same for His prayers for His Disciples and for all believers.

PRAYER FOR ALL BELIEVERS
Mark 14:36, Luke 22:42. Jesus knew He would have to die and prayed that He wouldn't have to suffer. He told God that He would do whatever God wanted and probably asked for the strength to endure what lay ahead.

PRAYER FOR DISCIPLES
John 17:11,14,15. Jesus knew His Disciples would be in danger because they believed in Him. He asked God to keep them safe, and that they would remain united in their faith.

PRAYER FOR ALL BELIEVERS
John 16:20-23,26. Jesus prayed that all who believed in Him would be filled with His spirit and His love and that they would be one so that the world would believe in Him and know God loves them.

You are one of the people Jesus prayed for in the garden. When you pray to the Father through Jesus, Jesus prays along with you. Draw a picture of yourself praying with Jesus.

SS842

JESUS' PRAYER

On the night before He died, Jesus prayed to God the Father. He prayed for Himself and for the Apostles. He also prayed for you and all the people who would believe in Him. Solve the rebus puzzle to find out the words Jesus said in His prayer. (John 17:20) Then read the rest of Jesus' prayer in John 17:21-26.

— —
 -PE    -G   -K   P+ -KE+Y    -U

— — — —
 -RE+   -AL    -BLO +E   -TON    -BL+  -AP

— — — —
 -U   T+   W+ -E    -HP+ -BA

— — —
 -L + -P + -ST   -P    -DAL

— — —
 -NE + -R +H    -RE + -FE    -M + D

SS842

ABBA, FATHER

Jesus used the word *Abba* when praying to God. In Aramaic, *abba* means "dear father" or even "dad." It is the word a child would have used when speaking to his own father. The Jews would have been upset if they had heard Jesus using *abba* instead of *abinu* (our father), but Jesus felt He had a close relationship with God and encouraged His Disciples to pray to God in the same way. Encourage the children to pray to God using the word *abba.* Help them to realize that they should feel just as comfortable talking to God as they do to their earthly fathers.

JESUS OBEYS HIS FATHER

Read Jesus' prayer in Mark 14:36. Ask the children if they have ever thought of Jesus having to obey His Father. How did Jesus obey His Father? Could Jesus have chosen to disobey God? How? Have the children consider that Jesus did not want to die on the cross. He chose to die out of love for us and obedience to God. Ask the children to suggest some ways they can follow Jesus' example of obedience in their own lives. Talk about why it is important to obey those in authority.

FOLLOWING JESUS' EXAMPLE

Jesus loved God so much that He obeyed Him, even though He knew it would cause Him pain. He loved us so much that He was willing to die on the cross for us. Jesus teaches that sometimes we have to suffer when we love someone, that sometimes love means having to do things we don't want to do. Think about some things you are asked to do that you don't like to do. Sometimes we do something because it will make someone happy, or because we know it is right. Draw a picture of yourself doing something you do not like to do because you are choosing to obey someone.

HELPING OTHERS

When Jesus prayed to His Father in the garden the night before He died, He asked God to take the "cup" of His death away from Him. He did not want to die, yet He chose to because He wanted us to have eternal life. Jesus knew that He would have to sacrifice His life for ours. By His example, Jesus teaches us that love means helping others even when it hurts us to do so. Have the children write a story about someone who wants to help another, but discovers he will have to do something he does not want to do. The children might like to illustrate their stories, or write them in play form and perform them for the class.

Shining Star Publications, Copyright © 1987, A division of Good Apple, Inc.

SS842

... NOT MY WILL,
BUT YOURS,
BE DONE.
Luke 22:42

OBJECTIVE: To visually represent Christ praying in the Garden of Gethsemane and His willingness to do what God the Father asked of Him.

MATERIALS: White poster paper, light green poster paper, an enlarged colored picture of Jesus praying in the garden, a yellow or gold marker, bright blue letters, and colored construction paper for student use.

PROCEDURE: Line the top half of the bulletin board with white poster paper and the bottom half with light green poster paper. Pin the picture and the letters in place. Use a yellow or gold marker to draw rays of light shining upon Jesus. Ask the children what the words on the bulletin board mean to them. Did Jesus want to suffer and die? Ask the children to think about a time when God answered their prayers in a way they did not want Him to. Sometimes God's plan for us is not what we would choose. Then we need to learn to pray like Jesus and be willing to accept God's will over our own. Give each child construction paper and have him cut out a flower or some other kind of plant to add to the garden. Suggest that as each child pins his plant to the bulletin board, he offer a silent prayer telling God how he will try to accept the unpleasant things that happen in his life.

SS842

TEACH US TO PRAY

One day Jesus was praying in a certain place. When He had finished, one of His Disciples said to Him, "Lord, teach us to pray . . . ." (Luke 11:1) Jesus taught them the words to the Lord's Prayer. Have the children pray the Lord's Prayer together. Ask them what the Lord's Prayer means to them. Most people know this prayer by memory but seldom think about what they are really saying. Have the children explore the meanings of the prayer by having them write it in their own words. The children might work in small groups with each group discussing and rewriting one sentence of the prayer and then sharing it with the class. Ask the children if they can find a line in the prayer that is similar to what Jesus prayed in the garden. ("Your will be done.") Talk about the importance of accepting God's will and about the need to forgive others.

THOUGHTS ABOUT PRAYER

In the New Testament, Jesus and His Disciples teach us many things about praying. Place the drawing of either the boy or the girl on one side of an 8½" x 11" paper and duplicate copies. Have each child search the New Testament for a teaching about prayer that has a special meaning for him. Have the child neatly letter the verse on his paper and color the praying child. Encourage the children to share their verses and the reasons for their choices with the class. Possible verses are Philippians 4:6; James 1:5,6; Mark 11:24; Mark 11:25; Psalm 62:8; Matthew 7:7-11; Matthew 6:5,6; Matthew 6:7,8; Matthew 26:41; Colossians 4:2; I John 1:8.

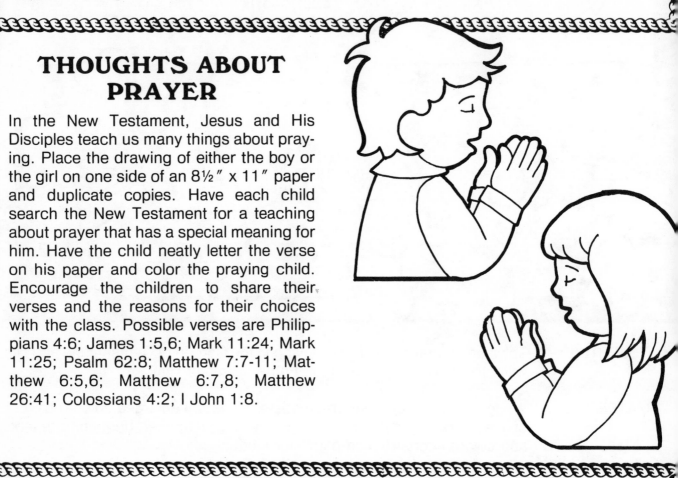

PERSISTENT PRAYER—Luke 18:1-8

One day Jesus told His Disciples a parable to teach them that they should always pray and never become discouraged. Read the parable of the widow and the judge to the children (using an easy-to-read Bible such as GOOD NEWS) or tell it to them in your own words. Talk about the meaning of the parable by asking such questions as: What did the widow keep doing? At first the judge refused to do anything. Why did he change his mind? What did the judge say about God? What does this parable tell you about praying? Help the children relate this parable to their own lives. Lead the children to the realization that sometimes we need to pray to God over and over about some things, but that we should not give up.

Shining Star Publications, Copyright © 1987, A division of Good Apple, Inc.

SS842

PRAYER ACTIVITIES
PRAYER TREE

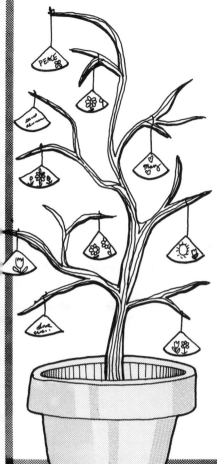

On the night before He died, Jesus prayed for many reasons. He asked God to bless the Apostles and give them courage. He prayed for all those who would believe in Him that they might be one in love, and He prayed for Himself. Because the Easter season is a special time of prayer, have the children think of people and causes they can pray for. Give each child a paper circle, about 2½ inches in diameter, that has been marked as shown. Have the child write a person or reason to pray for on the circle. Cut a slit in the circle along the solid line. Fold along the dotted line. Turn the circle over and decorate the other side. Then pull the folded portion of the circle underneath to form a cone shape and glue it in place. Secure it with a paper clip until dry. Knot one end of a string and run the other end through the center of the cone. Form a loop at the top. Hang the cones on a tree branch. Each day, choose a cone from the tree as a prayer idea.

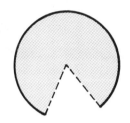

PERSONAL BOOK OF PRAYERS

Children might enjoy creating their own personal prayer books. Write each prayer on a separate page and decorate the page as desired. Add a cover, and staple the pages together. Possible prayer topics could include

A Prayer for When I'm Happy
A Prayer for When I'm Sad
A Prayer for Forgiveness
A Prayer for When I'm Angry
A Prayer for When I'm Confused
A Prayer for Peace
A Prayer for Thanks
A Prayer for When I Need Help
A Prayer Just to Tell God That I
   Love Him

Allow the children to share their prayers if they want to, or let them keep them private.

SS842

PANTOMIME PRAYER CIRCLE

When Jesus' friend Lazarus died, Jesus raised him from the dead. He prayed to God before he called Lazarus from the tomb. Read John 11:41,42 to find out what Jesus said. Be sure the children understand that Jesus prayed to thank His Father. We too have many things for which to be thankful. Ask the children to think of some things for which they are grateful. Then gather the children together in a prayer circle. Begin the prayer with these words: ''Dear Father, You have given us many things. We have much to thank You for.'' Have each child (and you too) pantomime one thing for which he would like to thank God. When everyone has finished, lead the children in singing a simple song of thanks. You might have the children use the music to the chorus of the song ''Amen'' and substitute the words ''thank you'' for all but the last amen.

GOD'S PLAN FOR YOU

The Easter season is a time when many people spend additional time reading the Bible and praying. Time spent in silent prayer is very important because it can help us to better understand God's plan. It is a time when we can listen to God with our hearts. Say a silent prayer to God. Then sit quietly for a few minutes. Draw a picture of one or two things you think God wants you to do this week. Put the picture in your room where you can see it every morning. Begin each day with a prayer asking God to help you do what He wants you to do.

SPECIAL EASTER PRAYERS

Easter is a special time for prayer. It is a time of sorrow because Jesus died and a time of rejoicing at His Resurrection. Have the children write their own special Easter prayers that express their feelings about Easter joy. Teach the children to print a few letters in a simple calligraphy style. They may then print their prayers on poster paper, using calligraphy for the initial letters of significant words like Jesus and Easter. If the children leave sufficient borders around their prayers, they might like to decorate them with joyful Easter symbols. Display the prayer posters where others may enjoy them as well.

SS842

AM I SLEEPING?

When Jesus went into the Garden of Gethsemane to pray, He knew His enemies were searching for Him. He knew it would not be long before the soldiers came to arrest Him, and He said to the Disciples, ''Stay here and watch while I pray.'' Then Jesus went further into the garden and cried out to His Father. So great was Jesus' agony that His sweat became like great drops of blood falling to the ground. But Jesus' Disciples could not stay awake while He suffered. Three times, Jesus returned to the Disciples and found them asleep.

Discuss the many times we are not really aware of the suffering that occurs in our world. Just like the Disciples, we too are sleeping. Have the children search newsmagazines and newspapers for pictures that show there is suffering in the world. Include in the range of photographs a child who is lonely and sad, and pictures of whole populations who are starving. Make a class collage of these pictures entitled ''Am I Sleeping While Others Suffer?'' Talk about things the children can do to help these people, including remembering them in their prayers every day.

A GIFT OF LOVE

Loneliness is a kind of suffering. Children might help shut-ins and the elderly. Talk to your local hospital to find out about the ''Meals on Wheels'' program in your area. Children could make the recipients of this program their special project by remembering them in their prayers and sending them cards or small gifts. These can be delivered with the meals. One possible gift is a plaque. Cut an 8″ x 6″ oval from white tagboard. Letter a saying like ''Jesus Loves You'' across the top. Make a cutout vase from a wallpaper sample. Cut flowers in three different shades and glue the three flower pieces together, one on top of another. Cut construction paper leaves, and use green pipe cleaners as stems. Cut a small circle for the center of each flower. Glue all pieces to the tagboard oval in an attractive arrangement. Add a pop-top ring to the back of the oval to serve as a hanger.

Patterns

SS842

HIDDEN APOSTLES

When the soldiers came to arrest Jesus in the Garden of Gethsemane, the Apostles were frightened; they ran away and hid. See if you can find the names of the Twelve Apostles hidden in this picture. Two of the Apostles have the same name. You will need to find that name twice.

SS842

JUDAS' BETRAYAL

Then one of the twelve, called Judas Iscariot, went to the chief priests and said, "What are you willing to give me if I deliver Him to you?" And they counted out to him thirty pieces of silver. So from that time he sought opportunity to betray Him.

While Jesus was in the garden . . . Judas, one of the twelve, with a great multitude with swords and clubs, came from the chief priests and elders of the people.

Now His betrayer had given them a sign, saying "Whomever I kiss, He is the One; seize Him."

Then immediately he went up to Jesus and said, "Greetings, Rabbi!" and kissed Him. And Jesus said to him, "Friend, why have you come?" Then they came and laid hands on Jesus and took Him.

Matthew 26:14-16, 47-50

Judas was the treasurer for the Disciples. Just why he chose to betray Jesus is not known, but it is likely that it was not for the money. The thirty pieces of silver he was given by the priests was only equal to a month's pay for a common laborer. Judas' betrayal was probably an attempt to force Jesus' hand so that Jesus would declare Himself a king and lead a rebellion against the Romans. Judas was not alone in expecting Jesus to be an earthly king, nor was he the only person who was disloyal to Jesus. The Jewish people themselves turned against Jesus when he was condemned, and even Peter denied knowing Him.

SS842

TRUE TREASURES

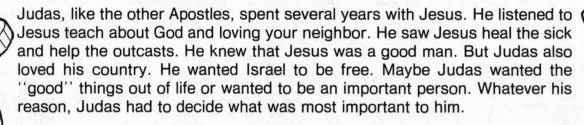

Judas, like the other Apostles, spent several years with Jesus. He listened to Jesus teach about God and loving your neighbor. He saw Jesus heal the sick and help the outcasts. He knew that Jesus was a good man. But Judas also loved his country. He wanted Israel to be free. Maybe Judas wanted the ''good'' things out of life or wanted to be an important person. Whatever his reason, Judas had to decide what was most important to him.

Like Judas, we have to make choices. We have to decide what is important to us—what our true treasures are. Number the coins from 1 to 10 (with 1 being the most important) to show the relative importance of these things in your life. Use gold to color the coins next to the five most important things.

Make a bar graph to show the choices of the class as a whole. Discuss the results.

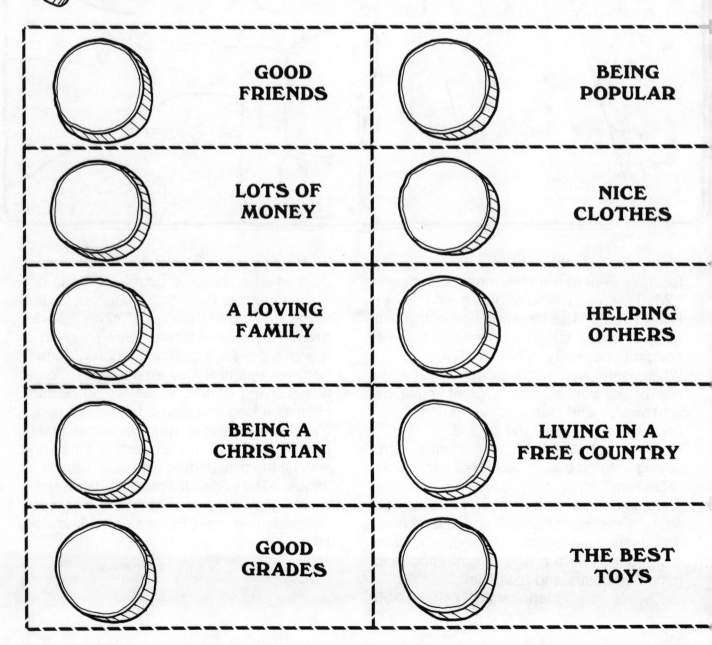

GOOD FRIENDS	BEING POPULAR
LOTS OF MONEY	NICE CLOTHES
A LOVING FAMILY	HELPING OTHERS
BEING A CHRISTIAN	LIVING IN A FREE COUNTRY
GOOD GRADES	THE BEST TOYS

SS842

TREASURE IN HEAVEN

In Luke 12:33,34, Jesus tells us to not worry about building up earthly treasures, but to ''provide yourselves money bags which do not grow old, a treasure in the heavens that does not fail . . . For where your treasure is, there your heart will be also.'' Most of the Disciples were able to follow Jesus' teaching, but Judas was more interested in worldly possessions. Follow each Disciple's path through the maze. Write *Judas* by the man who followed the wrong path. Write another Apostle's name by the man who made the right choice.

START

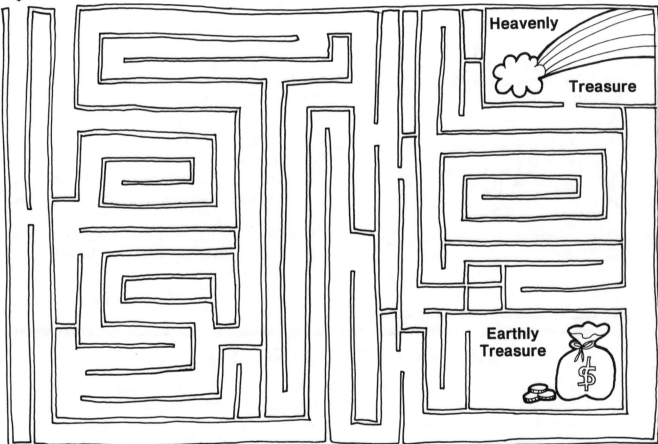

Read the parable of the Rich Young Ruler in Matthew 19:16-22 to the children. The rich young ruler was a good man. He was willing to do all that Jesus asked of him except for one thing. What did Jesus ask him to do that he would not do? In some ways, Judas was like the rich young ruler. He was more interested in earthly things than in laying up treasure in heaven. Have the children draw simple mazes with Jesus at the center. Ask the children to draw simple scenes along the correct path that show some of the things we can do to build a path to Jesus. Allow time for the children to solve some of their classmates' mazes.

THE KINGDOM OF JESUS

Like many other people, Judas probably expected Jesus to become the king of Israel and drive out the Romans. He was disappointed when Jesus did not establish Himself as an earthly king. Jesus, however, said, ". . . My kingdom is not of this world . . . ." (John 18:36) The kingdom Jesus established for us is a heavenly kingdom, and the true treasure of that kingdom is Jesus Himself.

Show the children a map. Discuss the kinds of symbols used on a map and how they are explained in the map's legend. Have the children design their own treasure maps that show the way to Jesus' kingdom. Have the children search the Scriptures for passages that tell us what we must do to enter into the kingdom of God. The children can then create their own symbols for use on their treasure maps and explain the meanings of the symbols in the map's legend. Some possible symbols might include the following:

♡ = Love one another as Jesus loved us.

🌧 = Love God with all your heart, with all your soul and with all your mind.

📖 = Obey the commandments.

✝ = Accept God's will.

To give the children's treasure maps an old, authentic look, have them crumple pieces of thin paper, smooth them out, and soak in a strong tea solution for a while. When the papers are dry, they can draw the maps with black markers. Allow time for the children to share their treasure maps with their classmates.

OBSTACLES ALONG THE WAY

Judas was more loyal to Israel than he was to Jesus. He wanted Jesus to be a powerful king who would free Israel from the Romans. Perhaps Judas also thought he would hold a place of honor when Jesus became king. These things were more important to him than living as Jesus wanted him to. Sometimes the things we want and the people we are loyal to can become so important to us that they become obstacles in our way to Jesus. Have the children draw obstacle courses to show some of the obstacles they themselves might have to overcome if they are to follow Jesus. Obstacles might include pressure from friends to do something wrong, playing hooky instead of going to church or school, etc. Allow time for the children to share their obstacle courses with others in small groups. Encourage them to talk about ways they can overcome these obstacles and live the way Jesus wants them to live.

SS842

PARABLE OF THE LOST COIN

Jesus told a story about a woman who searched for a coin she had lost. This story illustrates to us how loyal God is to each of us even when we disobey Him. Have several children pantomime this parable.

—Characters—
Woman, Several Friends

—Props—
Table, Box with 9 pennies, Several containers, Two chairs,
Basket on floor, One penny behind basket

WOMAN: Enters room. Picks up a box from the table. Opens box. Takes out coins and counts them. Looks confused. Counts coins again. Looks upset and worried. Looks under table. Looks in other containers, turning each upside down to see if anything falls out. Looks more upset. Moves furniture, looking under each piece. Finally finds coin behind basket. Looks happy. Kneels and says a prayer. Goes to door. Cups hand alongside mouth. Calls friends.

FRIENDS: Enter room. Give questioning looks to woman.

WOMAN: Shows them the coin. Goes to table and points to box. Holds up nine fingers. Looks under table and in another container. Points to basket. Holds up coin.

(Based on Luke 15:8-10)

Ask a volunteer to explain what happened in the pantomime. Ask the children: What lesson was Jesus trying to teach with this story? How is each of us like the lost coin? How can we be lost from God? Lead the children to the realization that even though God has many people who believe in Him, each person is very special to God. When we stray from God through sin, He does not give up on us. When we are sorry for our sin, God welcomes us back with open arms. Have a child read Luke 15:10 to the class.

SS842

OUR COUNTRY'S COINS

The coins of a nation frequently show something about that country's loyalties. Look at the five U.S. coins below. They tell us something about the things our country stands for.

What one word is printed on all our coins? _ _ _ _ _ _ _ _

What does it tell you about our country? _____

_____

In 1955, the government passed a law saying that a motto must be printed on United States money. What motto is printed on the coins?

_ _ _ _ _ _ _ _ _ _ _ _ _ _ _

What does this tell you about our country? _____

_____

The picture of a president is printed on each coin. Use the number code (1 = A, 2 = B, 3 = C) to find out each president's name. Then tell why you think his picture was chosen for the coin.

$\overline{1}\ \overline{2}\ \overline{18}\ \overline{1}\ \overline{8}\ \overline{1}\ \overline{13}$

$\overline{12}\ \overline{9}\ \overline{14}\ \overline{3}\ \overline{15}\ \overline{12}\ \overline{14}$

_____

_____

$\overline{20}\ \overline{8}\ \overline{15}\ \overline{13}\ \overline{1}\ \overline{19}$

$\overline{10}\ \overline{5}\ \overline{6}\ \overline{6}\ \overline{5}\ \overline{18}\ \overline{19}\ \overline{15}\ \overline{14}$

_____

_____

$\overline{6}\ \overline{18}\ \overline{1}\ \overline{14}\ \overline{11}\ \overline{12}\ \overline{9}\ \overline{14}$

$\overline{18}\ \overline{15}\ \overline{15}\ \overline{19}\ \overline{5}\ \overline{22}\ \overline{5}\ \overline{12}\ \overline{20}$

_____

_____

$\overline{7}\ \overline{5}\ \overline{15}\ \overline{18}\ \overline{7}\ \overline{5}$

$\overline{23}\ \overline{1}\ \overline{19}\ \overline{8}\ \overline{9}\ \overline{14}\ \overline{7}\ \overline{20}\ \overline{15}\ \overline{14}$

_____

_____

$\overline{10}\ \overline{15}\ \overline{8}\ \overline{14}$

$\overline{11}\ \overline{5}\ \overline{14}\ \overline{14}\ \overline{5}\ \overline{4}\ \overline{25}$

_____

_____

(Answers are found on page 144.)

90

SS842

LOYALTY AND FRIENDSHIP

The thirty pieces of silver Judas received symbolize his disloyalty to Jesus. Have the children share their thoughts about what loyalty and friendship mean. Emphasize the significance of what Jesus called Judas in Matthew 26:50.

The Scriptures provided will give the answer to the question asked in each letter. When all the questions have been answered, cut out the two rows of letters and attach them to a sheet of heavy paper or light cardboard. Hang the friendship poster where everyone can enjoy it.

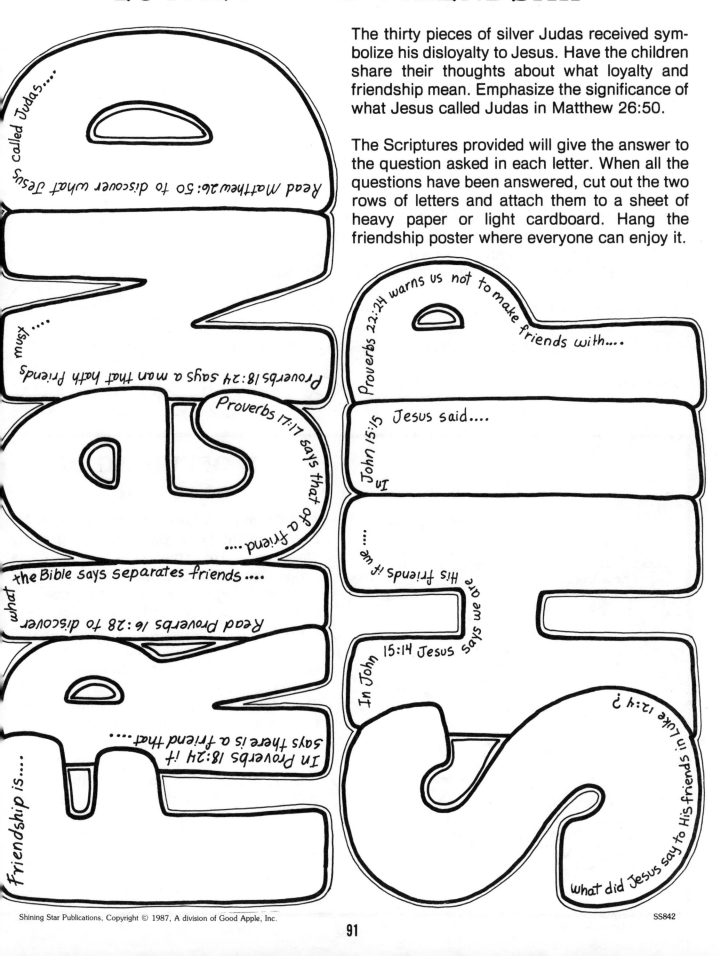

SS842

JUDAS REPENTS

Then Judas, His betrayer, seeing that He (Jesus) had been condemned, was remorseful and brought back the thirty pieces of silver to the chief priests and elders, saying, "I have sinned by betraying innocent blood." And they said, "What is that to us? You see to it!" Then he threw down the pieces of silver in the temple and departed, and went and hanged himself.

Matthew 27:3-5

When Judas realized how wrong he had been, he returned the thirty pieces of silver to the temple and confessed his sin. In the parable of the Lost Coin, Jesus taught that the angels of God would rejoice over a sinner who repents. Ask the children if they think Jesus forgave Judas for betraying Him. Was it dangerous for Judas to return the money to the temple and tell the priests that Jesus was innocent? (Jesus had not yet been crucified, but He had been condemned to death for treason against the Roman government. Judas himself could have been accused of the same crime.) Ask the children if it takes courage to admit you've done something wrong. Ask the children to suggest times they might have to—or want to—confess something they did, even if it means they might be in trouble (breaking a window, cheating on a test, etc.).

AN OFFERING OF SILVER

An effective offering from the children for Easter might be a bag containing thirty silver coins. This could be done as a class project or on an individual basis. If each child is willing to contribute thirty coins, it would be especially effective. Give each child a piece of net about seven inches square and a piece of string. The coins can be placed in the center of the net, and the net brought up and tied to resemble a bag. The silver coins contributed by the children can be any denomination, or they can be pennies wrapped in aluminum foil to look like silver coins. With the permission of the pastor, the children can place their thirty pieces of silver at the foot of the cross (perhaps as part of the Good Friday services) as a sign of their willingness to remain loyal to Jesus.

SS842

PETER'S DENIAL

Then Jesus said to them, "All of you will be made to stumble because of Me this night, for it is written:

'I will strike the Shepherd, and the sheep of the flock will be scattered.'

But after I have been raised, I will go before you to Galilee." Peter answered and said to Him, "Even if all are made to stumble because of You, I will never be made to stumble."

Jesus said to him, "Assuredly, I say to you that this night, before the rooster crows, you will deny Me three times."

Matthew 26:31-34

Peter was the least expected of those who played a part in the death of Jesus. Peter was one of the three Disciples who were closest to Jesus. He really loved Jesus and was sure he would never do anything to hurt Him, even when Jesus told him that he would. Yet Peter denied Jesus not once, but three times in just a few short hours.

For hundreds of years, a rooster crowing at dawn has been a signal to wake up and begin a new day. When the rooster crowed during the trial of Jesus, it reminded Peter of Jesus' words about his denial. It woke Peter up to the fact that he had denied his friend and made him realize that his faith was not as strong as he thought it was.

SS842

THE ROOSTER CROWED

Read the story of Peter's denial in Luke 22:54-62. Then do the crossword puzzle. All the answers are in this passage.

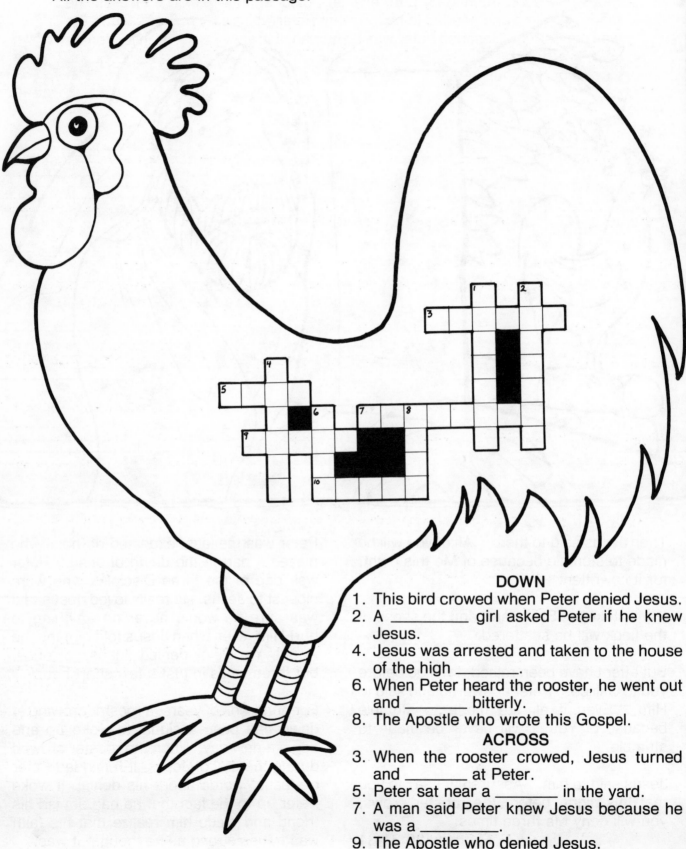

DOWN

1. This bird crowed when Peter denied Jesus.
2. A _____ girl asked Peter if he knew Jesus.
4. Jesus was arrested and taken to the house of the high _____.
6. When Peter heard the rooster, he went out and _____ bitterly.
8. The Apostle who wrote this Gospel.

ACROSS

3. When the rooster crowed, Jesus turned and _____ at Peter.
5. Peter sat near a _____ in the yard.
7. A man said Peter knew Jesus because he was a _____.
9. The Apostle who denied Jesus.
10. The number of times Peter said he didn't know Jesus.

SS842

THE ROOSTER—SYMBOL OF PETER

Peter had good intentions, but he often acted without thinking. Like us, he made mistakes and needed to be forgiven. Peter was a very human person; he was not perfect. Because Peter was so human, it is easy for children to identify with him. Read Scripture passages that deal with Peter and think about the kind of person he was.

"WE SAY WE LOVE HIM"
Words and Music by Helen Friesen

We say we love Him, we try to serve Him, still we at times may fall
Ju-das be-trayed Him, Pe-ter de-nied Him, Be-fore the cock did crow
No-tice the guilt that Ju-das then car-ried No mon-ey could e-rase,
Pe-ter re-pent-ed, wept tears of an-guish, Watched how His mas-ter bled,

Let's not for-get that Je-sus can hear us no mat-ter when we call.
While they were sin- ing, Je-sus still loved them, How could they hurt him so?
Tried to re-turn it, but they re-fused it, His life he could not face.
Je-sus for-gave him, gave him a mis-sion, "Go feed my lambs," He said.

SS842

THE PRODIGAL SON

Read Luke 15:11-32, and answer these eleven questions. Print the letters of each word on the spaces by each question. In the puzzle below, print the letters in the boxes on the lines that correspond to the correct numbers.

1. The younger son asked his father for his share of the _____
2. What did he do with his share? (_____ it)
3. What bad thing happened in that country?
4. What animals did the son have to feed so he wouldn't starve?
5. The younger son decided he would ask his _____ to hire him as a servant.
6. What did the father do when his son came home? (_____ him)
7. What did the son tell his father he had done?
8. What animal did the father kill when his son came home?
9. The father prepared a _____ to celebrate his son's return.
10. How did the older son feel when the younger son was treated so well?
11. The father told his older son to be happy because his brother was _____.

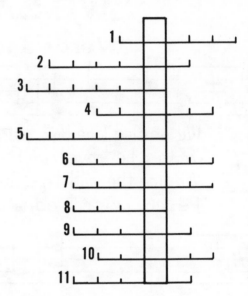

This story is all about $\underline{\hphantom{x}}$ $\underline{\hphantom{x}}$ $\underline{\hphantom{x}}$ $\underline{\hphantom{x}}$ $\underline{\hphantom{x}}$ $\underline{\hphantom{x}}$ $\underline{\hphantom{x}}$ $\underline{\hphantom{x}}$ $\underline{\hphantom{x}}$ $\underline{\hphantom{x}}$ $\underline{\hphantom{x}}$.

    8 1 5 10 4 11 3 7 2 6 9

Jesus told this story to teach us that God is always willing to forgive us and to share His love with us even when we do things we shouldn't. Ask the children how the father is like God. Do both of the sons need to be forgiven? Why? (The older son is jealous and doesn't rejoice that his brother is alive.) What is the difference between the two sons? (The younger saw that he was wrong and asked for forgiveness.)

Have the children suggest ways that Peter was like the prodigal son. Like him he, too, needed forgiveness. Peter had promised to stand by Jesus even if it meant he might die. He was too proud to admit he might be weak. Like the father in the story, Jesus was willing to forgive Peter for his sin. When He returned to the apostles after His Resurrection, Jesus made Peter the leader of the disciples.

Shining Star Publications, Copyright © 1987, A division of Good Apple, Inc.

SS842

ROOSTER REMINDERS

A rooster crowing awakened Peter to the realization that he had denied Jesus. Children might make roosters as reminders to "stay awake" in their own faith and trust in Jesus.

TRANSLUCENT ROOSTER

Duplicate the rooster pattern on 9″ x 12″ red construction paper, so each child has a copy. To make the rooster, carefully cut out the inside portion of the bird. The inner section will be discarded, so it doesn't matter if it is damaged. Turn the paper over. Place a sheet of red tissue paper over the opening and glue it in place. When the paper has dried, carefully cut out the rooster along the outline. A light coating of cooking oil can be rubbed over the tissue paper to make it more translucent if desired, although the effect is pretty without it. Hang the rooster in a window where the light can shine through it.

MOSAIC ROOSTER

Wallpaper samples can be used to create a beautiful mosaic rooster. Check with your local paint and wallpaper store about obtaining an outdated sample book. Duplicate the rooster pattern on 9″ x 12″ white construction paper. Provide wallpaper samples in a variety of colors and designs for the children to use. Give the children an opportunity to decide which wallpaper samples they wish to use for the various sections of the roosters. Children should work on one section at a time. Cut the wallpaper into small, irregularly-shaped pieces. Paint one section of the rooster with white glue. Immediately stick the mosaic pieces in place and press them down. Don't place the pieces too close together; allow some of the background to show. If desired, the children might color in grass and sky as a background for their mosaic roosters.

SS842

BE A CHICKEN "EGGS"-PERT

The chicken is the most valuable bird in the world. It descended from the red jungle fowl found in southeast Asia. King Solomon's men brought such birds to Israel from India, Burma and Malaya. At the time of Christ, chickens were raised for food and were kept in courtyards for convenience. The hen's care of her eggs and chicks was often seen as a symbol of love (Jesus uses this idea when he laments Jerusalem), and the rooster, because of its fighting ability, was a symbol of vanity and courage.

Find out more about chickens by filling in the missing words. The number of spaces tells you the number of letters in each word. Find the words on the eggs.

Did you know that there are more chickens on Earth than there are

(1)_ _ _ _ _ _? A male chicken is called a (2) _ _ _ _ _ _ _

and a female chicken is called a (3) _ _ _. Every chicken begins life

as an (4)_ _ _. The hen keeps the egg (5) _ _ _ _ for 21 days.

The (6) _ _ _ _ provides food for the chick while it grows inside the egg. When

the chick fills up the egg, it uses its (7) _ _ _ _ to break through the (8) _ _ _-

_ _ _ _ _. A baby chick is covered with furry down (9) _ _ _ _ _ _-

_ _ _. Many baby birds need to get food from their (10) _ _ _ _ _ _ _,

but a baby chick is ready to find its own food soon after it has

(11) _ _ _ _ _ _ _. By the time it is six weeks old, a chick has lost

its (2) _ _ _ _ and has grown 8,500 true feathers. When it is five

months old, a hen can start (13) _ _ _ _ _ _ eggs.

LAYING
FEATHERS
PARENTS
HEN

BEAK
ROOSTER
YOLK
WARM
EGG

HATCHED
EGGSHELL
PEOPLE
DOWN

SS842

AS A HEN WITH HER CHICKS

Procedure:
Cover the bulletin board with white paper. Enlarge the hen to an appropriate size for your board. Color the hen with markers and position it in the center of the board. The verse, "O Jerusalem . . . . How often I wanted to gather your children together, as a hen gathers her chicks under her wings . . . ." (Matthew 23:37) may be added. If necessary enlarge the chick pattern. Duplicate the chick on white cards so that each child has one. Have each child color the chick's beak and legs orange and the grass green. Tell each to glue yellow cotton balls to the chick, spreading out the cotton to form the tail feathers. Have him add a sequin eye and print his name at the top of the card. Pin the chicks near both ends of the board. As the children memorize verses from Scripture, they can move their chicks closer to the hen.

Read Matthew 23:37-39 to the children. Let them share their opinions on what the verse means. Explain to the children that Jesus was very sad because the people of Jerusalem were not willing to listen to His word. They killed the prophets God had sent to speak to them. They threw stones at God's other messengers who tried to teach them. They even tried to stone Jesus. Talk about how Jesus wants to be close to each one of us, but He can't if we won't let Him. Talk about ways we keep Jesus at a distance. Discuss ways the children can be close to Jesus in their daily lives. Help the children to realize that no matter what they have done to keep Jesus out of their lives, He is always willing to forgive them and gather them together under His "wings."

Tell the children that one way we can get closer to Jesus is by learning what He says to us in the Scriptures and by following His teachings in our lives. Provide Scripture verses for the children to memorize.

SS842

THE "EGGS"-CITING EGG

The egg is a universal symbol of new life. As an Easter symbol, the shell is compared to a tomb in which the beginning of life (the chicken embryo) is imprisoned until the time when the new life (chick) breaks forth from within the shell and enters the world. Decorated eggs at Easter can be a reminder to us that new life comes to those who believe in Jesus. Allow time for the children to decorate eggs with religious symbols and the letters *XV* (which mean ''Christ is risen'').

SYMBOL OF THE TRINITY

Easter is a good time to talk to the children about the Trinity. Since this is a difficult concept for children to understand, use an egg as a symbol of the Trinity. Explain that just as there are three parts—the shell, the white and the yolk—in one egg, there are three persons—the Father, the Son and the Holy Spirit—in one God. Ask the children to suggest some ways God the Father is like the eggshell. (He protects us. He sent His Son so that we could have new life.) Ask the children how Jesus might be like the egg white. (White is the color of purity and innocence. Jesus was without sin.) Just as the egg white contains the yolk—the food source for the developing chick—so Jesus came as the source of new life for us. After He returned to Heaven, Jesus sent the Holy Spirit to be with us. Ask the children how the yolk of an egg might represent the Holy Spirit. (In order to grow, the chick within the egg needs nourishment. It gets this from the yolk. If we are to grow spiritually we need the power of the Holy Spirit within us.)

SYMBOL OF FORGIVENESS

When a chick is ready to emerge from the egg, it jabs at the inside of the shell with a special egg tooth on its beak. It may take anywhere from twenty minutes to fourteen hours for the chick to break through the shell enough to enter the world. In some ways, the egg might be thought of as a symbol of forgiveness. When we are angry or upset with someone and have not forgiven him, we are trapped inside a shell. We need to find it in our hearts to forgive if we are to be set free. Sometimes it is easy to forgive someone who has hurt us, but at other times it is difficult for us to forgive and we have to really work at it, just as the chick needs to really work at breaking out of the eggshell. Ask each child to think of someone he needs to forgive. Have him write that person's name (in code if he wishes) on a paper egg. Have the children put the eggs where they can see them every day. Ask them to try to reach out to those people in forgiveness each day.

100
SS842

CROWN HIM WITH MANY CROWNS

Then the soldiers of the governor took Jesus into the Praetorium and gathered the whole garrison around Him. And they stripped Him and put a scarlet robe on Him. When they had twisted a crown of thorns, they put it on His head, and a reed in His right hand. And they bowed the knee before Him and mocked Him, saying, ''Hail, King of the Jews!''   Matthew 27:27-29

Soldiers did not mock Jesus because he was Jesus, but because of His claim to be a king. The act of placing a crown of thorns and a robe on Jesus was what would have been done to anyone claiming to be a king. According to Roman law, Jesus was guilty of treason. This was considered the most serious of crimes, and the punishment was crucifixion. The sign placed over the cross on which Jesus was crucified read ''King of the Jews.'' The Sadducees had asked that the sign be changed to read, ''He says he is the King of the Jews,'' but Pilate refused to change it.

Shining Star Publications, Copyright © 1987, A division of Good Apple, Inc.

SS842

A LILY AMONG THORNS

"Like a lily among thorns, So is my love . . . ."   Song of Solomon 2:2

At His trial, the soldiers mocked Jesus by plaiting thorns into a mock crown and placing it on His head. Jesus not only endured the pain of the thorns, but the pain of insult during the trial. The crown of thorns is a symbol of the suffering Jesus endured during His last week on Earth.

THORNY PLANTS

In botany, a thorn is a short, hard, sharp-pointed, leafless branch. Thorns develop on many different kinds of plants. Examples of plants with thorns are vines such as the catbrier and the sweetbrier (a type of wild rose), blackberry, raspberry and rose bushes, woody plants like hawthorn and locust trees, desert plants like cacti, and nonwoody plants like thistles. Have the children bring in pictures of plants that have thorns. Ask the children to suggest reasons why God created such plants to have thorns. Lead the children to the realization that thorns help to protect these plants from plant-eating animals. Point out that while thorns can cause us to suffer (when we prick a finger or our legs get scratched), the thorny plants produce some beautiful flowers and delicious fruits.

BEAUTY IN SUFFERING

When we suffer, our bodies hurt or we feel bad inside. During times like that, it's hard to see how anything good can come from suffering. Yet suffering is much like a thorny plant. Ask the children how they know when they are happy. Point out that if they had never been sad, they would not know what happiness was. Ask the children to think back to times they have suffered in their lives. Can they think of anything good that came out of that pain? Like thorns on plants, suffering is a kind of protection. Once we have experienced pain, we know what it means to suffer, and we avoid doing dangerous things that could hurt us. Suffering also makes us stronger. Help the children to understand that while Jesus endured enormous suffering during His passion and death, the end result was the most beautiful thing. Jesus rose again to a new life—a life without pain or suffering and with eternal happiness with God—a new life that He won for us, too.

Shining Star Publications, Copyright © 1987, A division of Good Apple, Inc.

SS842

THE THORNS AND THE LILY

And they clothed Him with purple; and they twisted a crown of thorns, put it on His head, and began to salute Him, "Hail, King of the Jews!"   Mark 15:17,18

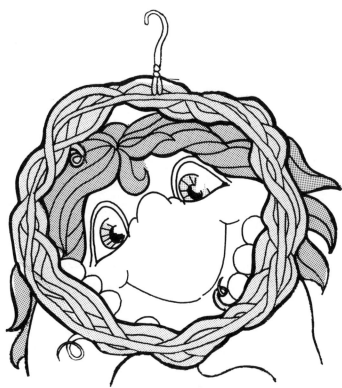

The crown of thorns the soldiers placed on Jesus' head is a symbol of both kingship and suffering. As a reminder that Jesus suffered and died for them so that they might have eternal life in the kingdom of Heaven, the children might make crowns of thorns. Grapevines, which are available in many craft stores, can be used to make interesting crowns of thorns to hang on the wall. (Because grapevines can be a little messy to work with, you might want to enlist the aid of some older students to help the children.) Soak the vines for about an hour until they are pliable. For each crown, loosely twist four or five vines together into a circle. Secure the vines by wrapping short pieces of thin copper wire around them at intervals. Allow the vines to dry thoroughly. Attach a wire hanger.

The lily has long been a symbol of purity and innocence. In Greek mythology, it was also the flower of peace. In Christian symbolism, the lily is often associated with Mary, with the archangel Gabriel, and with Christ. Because the lily is one of the first flowers of spring, it is frequently associated with Jesus' death and Resurrection. The pure white petals signify His innocence; Jesus had committed no sin. The gold anthers signify the divine light that encompasses the risen Lord. At Easter, the children could decorate their crowns of thorns with paper lilies. Duplicate the lily pattern on white paper. Give these directions to each child: color the anthers gold. Cut out the lily. Overlap one end of the lily over the other end at the dotted line. Glue in place. Knot the end of a pipe cleaner. Insert the pipe cleaner through the hole in the lily with the knot inside. Decorate your crown with your lilies.

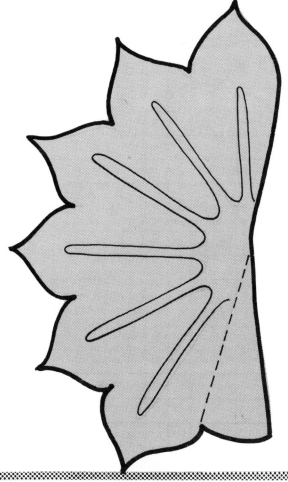

A CROWN OF VICTORY

"Blessed is the man who endures temptation; for when he has been proved, he will receive the crown of life which the Lord has promised to those who love Him."   James 1:12

Throughout the New Testament, Christians are told to be on their guard against temptation. When Jesus prayed in the garden, He told the Disciples, "Watch and pray, lest you enter into temptation."   Mark 14:38

After Jesus was baptized in the Jordan, the Spirit led Him into the desert to be tempted by the Devil. Organize the children into three groups. Assign each group one of the temptations in Matthew 4:1-11, and have them prepare a short skit depicting Jesus being tempted. Some children in each group might be the actors and others might draw the scenery. After each group has performed its skit, have the children suggest some reasons why God would allow Jesus to be tempted by the Devil.

In The Lord's Prayer we pray, "lead us not into temptation." Ask the children to define temptation in their own words. Have them suggest ways children their age can be tempted. Possibilities might be temptations to lie, to steal, to copy someone else's homework, to pick on or make fun of another child, to be selfish, and so on. Have each child pair up with a classmate and choose a kind of temptation to write about. Each child then writes the beginning of a story in which a child is tempted. The children then trade papers with their partners, and the partners complete the stories by showing a way the child could resist the temptation. Partners then switch papers again and read what the other child has written. Or, share the stories as a group.

SS842

CROWNS OF LIFE

Jesus truly is a king, but His kingdom is not of this world. Lead the children to understand that Jesus could have saved Himself if He had said that He was not King of the Jews, but He chose not to. Like a true king, Jesus was willing to sacrifice Himself for the sake of His people.

Words and Music by Helen Kitchell Evans
Frances Mann Benson

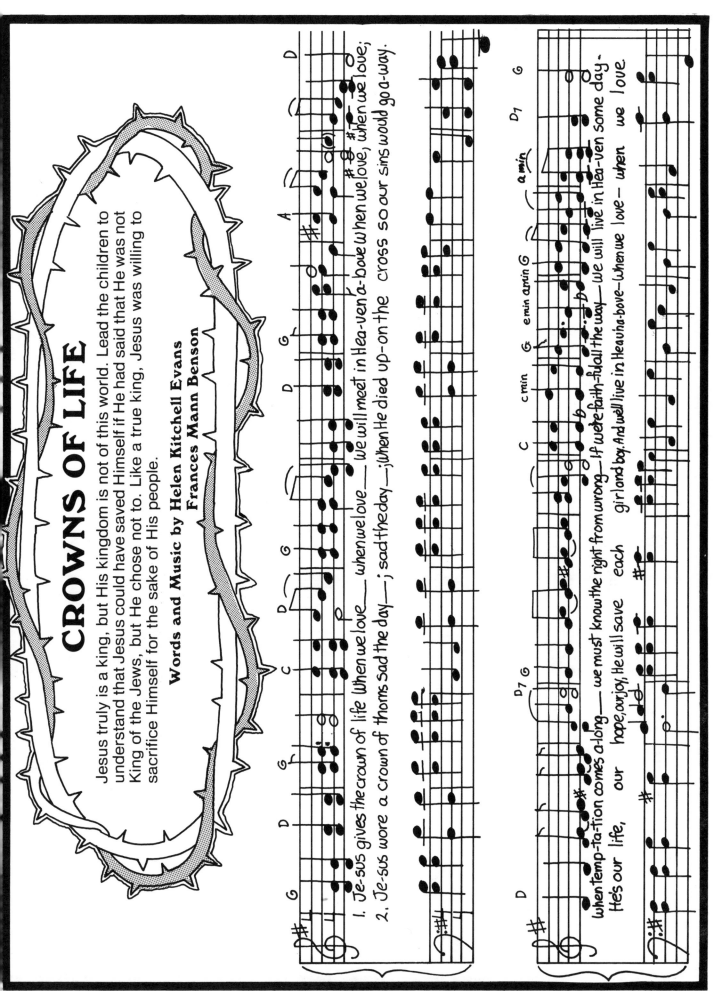

SS842

THE CROWN OF FREEDOM

"Bless the Lord, O my soul . . . Who redeems your life from destruction, Who crowns you with lovingkindness and tender mercies."

Psalm 103:1,4

Many Jewish people hoped Jesus had come as the Messiah, a king who would free Israel from the Romans. But Jesus came to establish a different kind of kingdom and to set people free from the power of evil. Jesus showed His power to do this by healing the sick, driving out demons and forgiving sins. Jesus taught us that true freedom can be found in serving God and others. He showed us that the Kingdom of God is a kingdom of freedom and love. Have the children work in groups of three or four to write songs that show how the kingdom Jesus came to establish is a kingdom of love and freedom. The children could make up their own melodies or set their lyrics to the tunes of familiar songs.

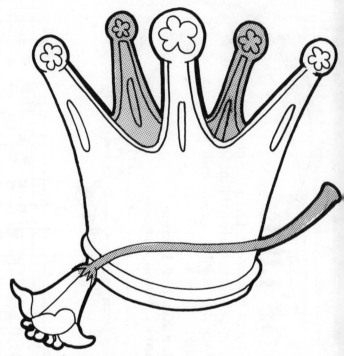

Jesus came to set us free to live as children of God. We help spread His kingdom on this Earth when we show our love for others in the things we say and do. Jesus tells us that if we are faithful, He will give us the "crown of life" (Revelation 2:10) and the keys to the Kingdom of Heaven.

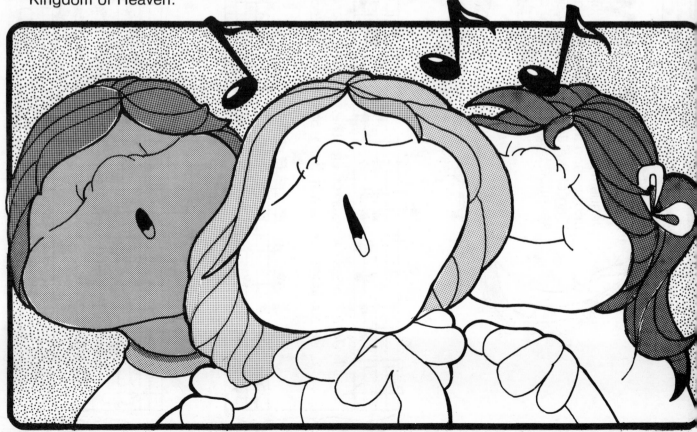

SS842

THE CROWN OF KINGSHIP

For many long years, the people of Israel had hoped that God would send them a great messiah-king who would establish himself as the king of the Jewish nation. Jesus was the Messiah they had been promised, but He avoided calling Himself ''Messiah'' because He knew the people expected a worldly king who would lead the Jews in a rebellion against the Romans, who occupied and controlled the nation. Remind the children how disappointed the people were when Jesus did not declare Himself the king. In Revelation 19:11-16, John tells us that Jesus will come again, not on a humble donkey, but as a glorious king.

''Then I saw heaven opened, and behold, a white horse. And He who sat on him was called Faithful and True . . . . and on His head were many crowns . . . . He was clothed with a robe dipped in blood . . . . And the armies in heaven, clothed in fine linen, white and clean, followed Him on white horses . . . . And He has on His robe . . . a name written:
> KING OF KINGS
> AND LORD OF LORDS.''

Draw a picture of Jesus coming to Earth as such a king.

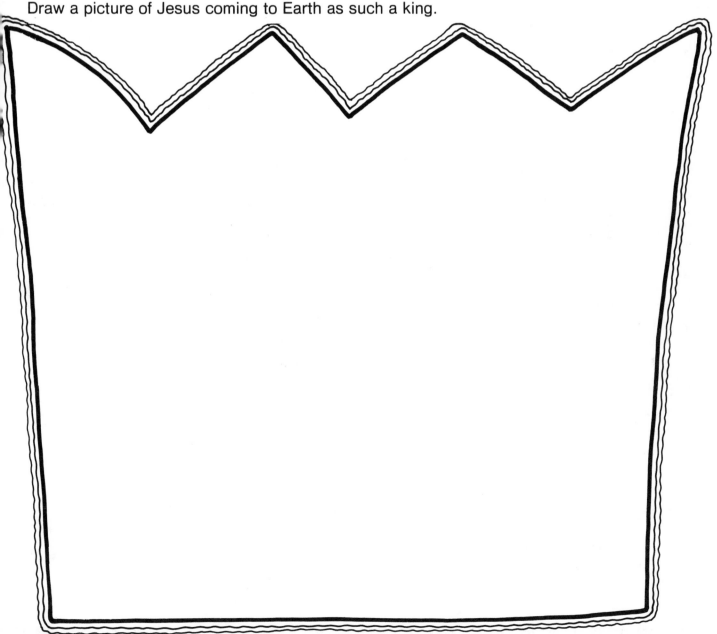

SS842

A STAR IN YOUR CROWN

For what is our hope, or joy, or crown of rejoicing? Is it not even you in the presence of our Lord Jesus Christ at His coming?   I Thessalonians 2:19

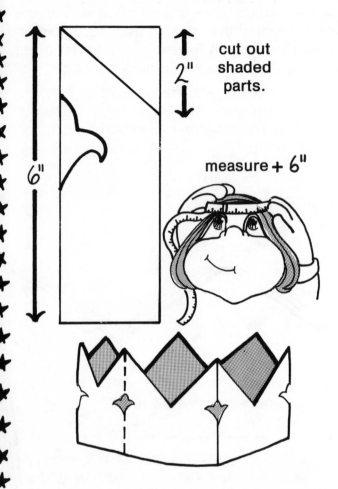

cut out shaded parts.

measure + 6"

Remind the children that through His death and Resurrection Jesus won for them the crown of eternal life. Have the children make paper crowns as signs that they are "the King's kids."

Give the children these directions:
Measure the distance around your head. Add ¼ of that distance to find the length of paper you will need. Cut a sheet of construction paper that length and 6 inches in height. Working from right to left, fold the paper in half three times. Measure two inches down from the top of the paper on the right side. Draw a line from that point to the upper left corner. Cut off that portion. Draw half a design, as shown, along the fold on the left side of the paper. Cut out the design, cutting through all layers. Open the paper. Place the center of the bottom edge against the center of your forehead. Bring the two ends around to overlap at the back of your head and match the end cuts to points in the crown. Glue in place.

Have you ever heard someone tell another person, "That's a star in your crown"? It is a way of saying that the person has done something that will bring him honor in some way. Often the phrase is used when someone has gone out of his way to help another or show kindness to him.

Suggest that the children might like to earn stars for their crowns by memorizing Scripture verses. Provide a list of references for verses or let the children pick their own. Each time a child has memorized a Scripture verse, give him a metallic star to stick on his paper crown. If you like, the child might earn two stars for finding and memorizing a Scripture verse containing the word "crown."

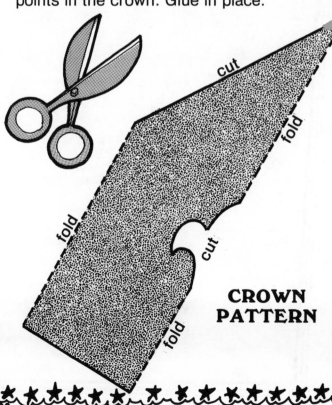

cut

fold

fold

cut

fold

CROWN PATTERN

LEGEND OF THE DOGWOOD

Many legends about plants have sprung up in connection with Christ's death and Resurrection. The anemone is said to have sprung up around the base of the cross, so it is marked with Jesus' blood. The thistle and the ilex are said to have been used to make the crown of thorns. According to the legend, Jesus Himself made the dogwood tree a reminder of His sacrifice for all people. Share this legend with the children. Then show them a picture of the dogwood flower or a real blossom and have them identify the markings.

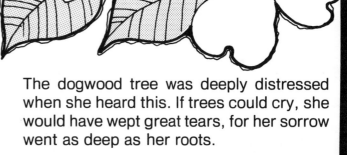

THE LEGEND OF THE DOGWOOD

Retold by
Kelly Riley

Many years ago, when Jesus was on Earth, the dogwood was a tall, sturdy, rugged tree. Sometimes, when Jesus wanted to be alone, He would rest in the shade of the dogwood tree. The tree grew very fond of Jesus because she recognized Him as a kind and gentle Man who loved all living things.

One day, a woodcutter and some Roman soldiers came into the glen where the dogwood tree grew. They stopped and looked carefully at the tall, straight tree. The dogwood tree felt very proud as she listened to the woodcutter tell the soldiers how strong her wood was.

"Well, Woodcutter," said one of the soldiers, "you have chosen wisely. We need strong wood for this cross."

"Yes," replied another soldier in a cruel voice. "It won't be long before we arrest Jesus of Nazareth, the so-called King of the Jews."

The dogwood tree was deeply distressed when she heard this. If trees could cry, she would have wept great tears, for her sorrow went as deep as her roots.

When Jesus came to the glen a few days later, He gazed sadly at the drooping boughs of the once proud tree, and He understood the dogwood's great sorrow. "Because of your pity for Me, I promise you that a dogwood tree will never suffer such a fate again."

From that day on, the dogwood tree has grown slender and crooked. No longer does it produce sturdy, rugged wood, but it bears beautiful, delicate cross-shaped flowers. The center of each white blossom is marked with a crown of thorns, and on the tip of each petal are red marks that look like nail prints. Since that time, the gentle dogwood tree has been a reminder to all who see it that Jesus died so that we could have new life.

SS842

I DON'T KNOW
Words and Music by
Kathy Jones

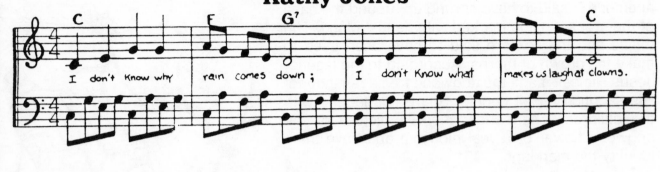

SS842

RESURRECTION MORNING

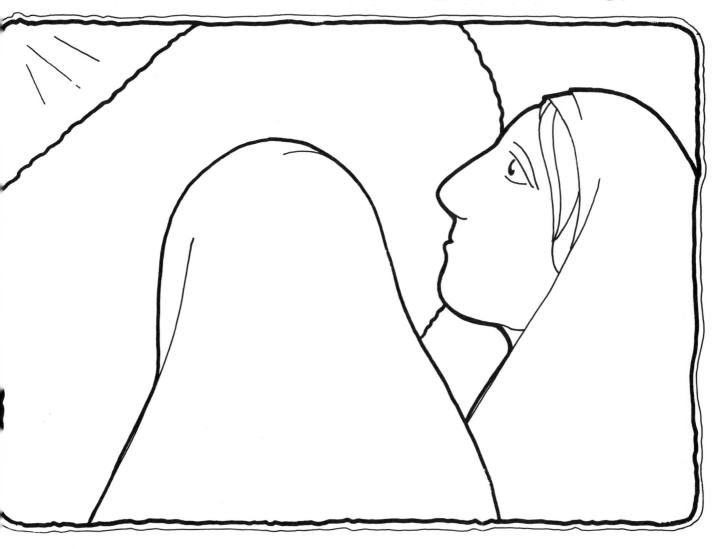

. . . as the first day of the week began to dawn, Mary Magdalene and the other Mary came to see the tomb. And behold, there was a great earthquake; for an angel of the Lord descended from heaven, and came and rolled back the stone from the door, and sat on it. His countenance was like lightning, and his clothing as white as snow . . . . But the angel answered and said to the women, ''Do not be afraid, for I know that you seek Jesus who was crucified. He is not here; for He is risen, as He said . . . .''
Matthew 28:1-6

Long before Jesus was born, God, speaking through the Prophet Isaiah, promised to send a valuable stone as a strong foundation for His people, and He promised that anyone who believed in this stone would not be disappointed. That stone was Jesus. Jesus' victory over death and His promise of eternal life set people free from the fear of death and guaranteed the forgiveness of sin.

While He lived as a man on Earth, Jesus could only be in one place at a time. Through His death and Resurrection, Jesus is able to be with each of us at all times.

SS842

THE LORD LIVES!
BLESSED BE MY ROCK!
(II Samuel 22:47)

On Easter Sunday we celebrate Jesus' Resurrection. The word *resurrection* means "coming to life again." Read this story of the first Easter, and fill in the missing words. The words are printed on the rocks at the bottom of the page.

(Based on Luke 24:1-12)

Very early in the morning, on the (1) _____ day after Jesus died,

Mary (2) _____, (3) _____, and (4) _____ the mother of

James went to the tomb where (5) _____ was buried. When they

got there, they saw that the (6) _____ in front of the tomb was

rolled away. The three women went into the tomb, but Jesus' (7)

_____ was not there. They were very puzzled. Suddenly, (8)

_____ men in bright shining clothes stood by them. The women

were very frightened. The men asked them, "Why are you looking

among the (9) _____ for one who is (10) _____? Don't you

remember that Jesus told you that He would be arrested, die on the

(11) _____, and three days later rise to (12) _____?" The

women ran from the tomb and told the (13) _____ Apostles the

wonderful news, but no one believed them. Then (14) _____

went to the tomb. He saw that it was empty and went home (15)

_____ at what had happened.

Jesus' Resurrection makes us feel (16) _____. Jesus showed us

that death is not the (17) _____ of life. It is the beginning of a

new life in (18) _____.

HEAVEN	MAGDALENE	BODY	JESUS	CROS
DEAD	THIRD	AMAZED	ALIVE	JOANNA	PETER	TW
MARY	ELEVEN	HAPPY	LIFE	END	STON

Shining Star Publications, Copyright © 1987, A division of Good Apple, Inc. SS84

HE IS NOT HERE;
FOR HE IS RISEN,
AS HE SAID.
Matthew 28:6

OBJECTIVE: To visually represent the concept that although Jesus died and was buried, He overcame death and rose to life again.

MATERIALS: Pale yellow poster paper; green letters; an enlarged, colored picture of the open tomb; colored construction paper for student use.

PROCEDURE: Cover the bulletin board with pale yellow poster paper. Pin the picture of the tomb and the letters in place. Discuss the fact that through His death and Resurrection, Christ has given us eternal life. Have the children suggest various signs of new life that are evident in the springtime. Possibilities include newborn animals, eggs, flowers, budding plants, butterflies, baby birds, and others. Provide the children with construction paper and scissors. Have each child cut out a small symbol of new life to add to the bulletin board.

Before placing symbols on the bulletin board, you may want to take the children for a walk and have them point out signs of new life that are springing up in nature. Explain that during fall and winter, things in nature die or seem to die. Leaves fall off the trees. Plants stop growing. Animals leave the area or go into hibernation and sleep through the winter. When spring comes, nature seems to be reborn. Trees bud. Birds return. Animals come out of their winter hiding places. Flowers bloom. Have the children compare these things with Jesus' death and Resurrection.

SS842

MY ROCK AND MY STRENGTH

Therefore thus says the Lord God: ''Behold, I lay in Zion a stone for a foundation, A tried stone, a precious cornerstone, a sure foundation . . . .''   Isaiah 28:16

In the Bible, the word *rock* (a large mass of stone) is used to create an image of strength, perseverance and security. As a metaphor for strength and endurance, the rock is a good choice. Ask the children what the word *rock* makes them think of. What other words do they associate with *rock*? Have the children make a list of times or places where a rock is used as an image of strength. Possible sources are songs, poems, hymns, Scripture verses, pictures or ads. After the children have had a chance to share and talk about the ways a rock represents strength, ask them to think about all the ways Jesus helps make them strong. Have them share their feelings about the strength Jesus gives them in whatever way they prefer—a poem, a story, a paragraph, a skit, a series of drawings— and give it the title ''Jesus—My Rock.''

Peter tells us that Jesus is ''a living stone'' (I Peter 2:4), a strong foundation on which we can build our faith and model our lives. That Jesus rose from the dead is the key fact of the Christian faith, the rock on which Christianity is built. We have not seen Jesus, but we know that He lives. As a class project (one that encourages working together), the children might make a large papier-mache rock. Make a base from chicken wire or several large balloons taped together. Soak newspaper strips in a water-flour paste and layer them on the base. Allow each layer to dry before adding another. Paint the rock tan, brown or gray. On one side of the rock, the children might paint an appropriate Scripture verse such as the one above. Display the rock near the entrance to the church. On Easter, the children could turn the rock over and paint ''He is risen! Alleluia!'' or another phrase on it. White burial cloths might be draped over it or placed alongside it.

Shining Star Publications, Copyright © 1987, A division of Good Apple, Inc.   SS842

BUILT ON A ROCK

One day Jesus told the crowd this parable: ". . . anyone who hears these words of mine and obeys them is like a wise man who built his house on rock. The rain poured down, the rivers flooded over, and the wind blew hard against that house. But it did not fall, because it was built on rock. But anyone who hears these words of mine and does not obey them is like a foolish man who built his house on sand. The rain poured down, the rivers flooded over, the wind blew hard against that house, and it fell. And what a terrible fall that was!"   Matthew 7:24-27 GOOD NEWS BIBLE

Have each child fold a sheet of 12" x 18" white construction paper in half and illustrate the parable. Tell each to show the wise man with his house on the rock on one side and the foolish man with his house on the sand on the other. Allow time for the children to share their drawings. Talk about why rock is a much better foundation for a house than sand is.

Explain that the objects in this parable all stand for other things. What does the rock stand for? What do the wind and the rain represent? Lead the children to understand that the words of Jesus are our rock. When we try to live our lives according to His words, we have the strength to resist sin and temptation. Jesus gives everyone a rock as a foundation for his house, but some people let the rock wear away so that it becomes weak like sand. (Sand is rock that has been broken down through physical changes known as weathering.)

Draw two groups of bricks on the chalkboard. Tell the children that our actions are the bricks we use to build our houses. What kinds of things do you think the person who obeys Jesus' words does? Print the actions on the wise man's bricks. How does the person who does not obey Jesus' words act? What kinds of things does he do? Print his actions on the foolish man's bricks. Explain that when a builder constructs a house, he uses mortar (cement) to hold the bricks together. Love is the mortar that holds our house together and makes it strong; but the person who disobeys Jesus' words has built a house without love, and so it is weak.

ROLL THE STONE AWAY

Rocks, stones and bricks are often used to keep things in or out. People build houses and other structures to keep out the weather and people who might intrude on them. Farmers build stone fences or walls to keep their herds from roaming away. Sometimes people build invisible walls around themselves so that other people cannot get close to them, or they put "stones" in front of their hearts so that they cannot love others. Through His death and Resurrection, Jesus showed us that we do not need to keep ourselves closed in. He set us free to live lives of love. As you sing this song, think about the ways you close your heart to other people and how you can open yourself up to those you meet.

ROLL THE STONE AWAY

Words and Music by Kelly Riley
Frances Mann Benson

1. When the an-gels rolled a-way the stone. With-in the tomb no bod-y lay shout for joy, Sing al-le-lu-ia. Christ our Lord lives for us to-day

2. Roll the stone a-way from your heart. For a bright-er day is dawn-ing In Christ we live and grow in love sing His praise this Eas-ter-morn.

SS842

Pretend that you are a newspaper reporter at the time of the first Easter. Pretend that you can interview Mary Magdalene, Peter and the other Disciple. Your job is to complete the front page of *The Stone Tablet*. Write headlines and stories, draw pictures, etc., to tell the story of Jesus' Resurrection. Read John 20:1-8 before you begin.

THE STONE TABLET
Easter, A.D. 33

PETER   OTHER DISCIPLE   MARY MAGDALENE

These three were the first to find out that Jesus had risen. Imagine their joy at finding that Jesus was alive! It shows in their faces!

SS842

STONE CRAFTS

ALLELUIA! HE IS RISEN!

A "stone" tomb can be made from an inverted plastic margarine tub. Children may make their own using small containers or may work as a class using a larger container. Use a good craft glue to cover the container with small stones and pebbles. Leave the "entrance" to the tomb uncovered, and paint it yellow (if the container is not that color). Glue a Popsicle stick to the back so that it sticks up above the rocks. Cut a sun shape from yellow tagboard and a cross from tan tagboard. Print a fitting verse on the cross and another on the sun. Attach the cross to the Popsicle stick with a reusable adhesive. Place a large stone in front of the opening to the tomb. Display the tomb. On Easter morning remove the cross, attach the sun, and move the stone away from the opening.

CINQUAIN STONES

A cinquain is a simple verse form. Have the children write cinquains expressing their feelings about Easter by following this form:

Line 1—Title (one word noun)
Line 2—Words or phrase that describes the title (two words)
Line 3—Action words or phrase about title (three words)
Line 4—A feeling about title (four words)
Line 5—Synonym for title (one word)

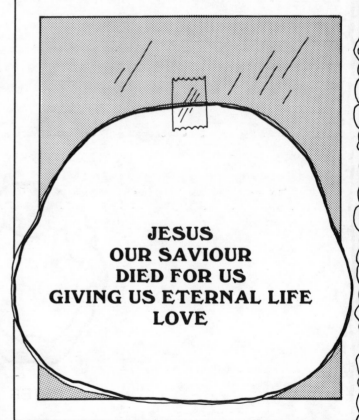

**JESUS
OUR SAVIOUR
DIED FOR US
GIVING US ETERNAL LIFE
LOVE**

Place a sheet of typing paper on a double layer of paper towels. Use another paper towel to coat both sides of the paper with cooking oil. Wipe off the excess oil. Let the paper dry on toweling for two days. Cut it into a stone shape. Print the cinquain on it with black ink or permanent marker. To make the stone shape look like it is made of stone, place it on a textured surface like a sidewalk or stucco wall. Use the side of a stick of gray chalk to lightly color the entire surface of the "stone." Display the translucent stones in the window where the light can shine through them.

Shining Star Publications, Copyright © 1987, A division of Good Apple, Inc.

ALLELUIA STONES

Have each child bring in an appropriately sized smooth stone. A white, light gray or black stone works best. (Suggest that the child wet the stone before bringing it to school to see if he likes the color. The color of the wet stone is the color it will be when varnished.) Have each child paint a favorite Scripture verse and Easter symbols on the stone with tempera paints. When the paint has dried, give each stone a coat of clear, high-gloss varnish. Let the stones dry overnight. The finished stones can be used as paperweights or as table decorations.

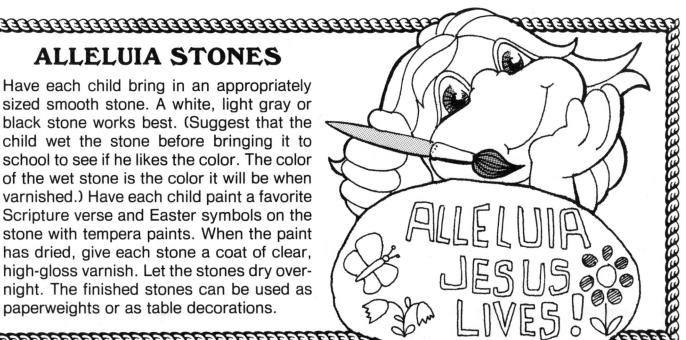

EMPTY TOMB GREETING CARDS

In Jesus' time, tombs were not underground but were hewn out of rock and the entrances blocked with large stones. Make a tomb card to send to friends in celebration of Christ's Resurrection or as an invitation to the Easter pageant (page 133). Cut the tomb shape from gray tagboard. Cut around the center stone, leaving a hinge on the straight side so that the stone can be folded back. Cut a sunburst shape from yellow paper and glue it in the center of a 3 1/4″ x 2 7/8″ black tagboard. Fold open the door and turn the tomb over. Glue the black card to the back of the tomb so that the sunburst can be seen through the opening from the front. An appropriate Scripture verse, such as Matthew 28:6 ("He is not here; for He is risen, as He said . . . .") or the invitation, may be printed on the sunburst.

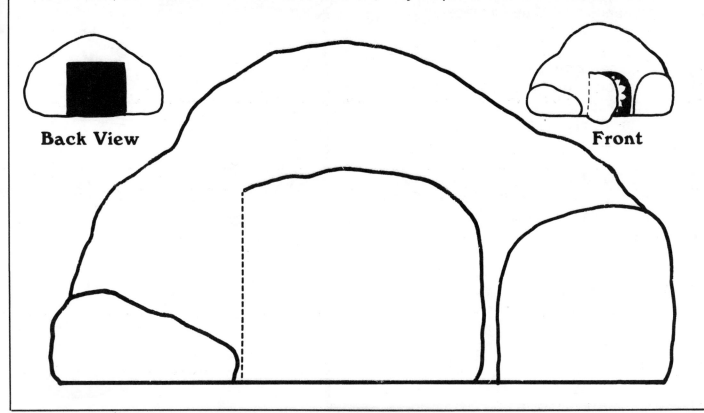

Back View

Front

STONE COOKERY

Sweet-smelling spices, such as myrrh, mint, and cinnamon, were popular in Bible times. They were brought by traders from Egypt, Mesopotamia and India and used in food, burned for worship, and placed in burial clothes. On Easter morning, when the women brought spices to anoint Jesus, they discovered that the tomb was empty. The children can celebrate Jesus' Resurrection by making a simple Easter bread.

Let a loaf of frozen bread dough rise in the refrigerator overnight. Tear off pieces of dough and roll them into small "stones" about the size of walnuts. Roll the stones in a cinnamon-sugar mixture and put them in a greased pan. Let the dough rise 20 minutes. Bake for 8 to 10 minutes at 400 degrees.

STONE SOUP

If Jesus came to Earth today, He might choose to tell a story like *Stone Soup* to teach you the importance of loving your neighbor and sharing with others. Read Marcia Brown's version of *Stone Soup* (Scribner's Sons, 1947) or another version written for young children. Before sharing the story with the children, ask each child to bring in an ingredient for soup. As you read the story to the children, make stone soup and have the children add their ingredients at the appropriate points in the story. Discuss the selfishness of the villagers at the beginning of the story and as the story progresses, talk about how they learned to share and work together.

RECIPE FOR STONE SOUP

3 clean, smooth stones
4 packages beef soup mix (boxed)
pinch salt and pepper
2 10-oz. packages sliced frozen carrots
1 head cabbage (cut up)
1 small beef roast (cooked and cut in bite-size pieces)
2 cans sliced Irish potatoes
1 cup milk

Place the stones in a large pan. Add the beef soup mix and 9 cups of water. Bring to a boil, stirring occasionally. Lower the heat and allow the soup to simmer. Add the remaining ingredients in the order indicated in the story. Allow the soup to simmer for 15 to 20 minutes after the cabbage has been put in. Serve with crackers or bread and butter. Yields approximately 20 servings. Remove the stones before serving the soup!

SS842

A SYMBOL OF FAITH

But when the morning had now come, Jesus stood on the shore; yet the disciples did not know that it was Jesus. Then Jesus said to them, "Children, have you any food?" They answered Him, "No." And He said to them, "Cast the net on the right side of the boat, and you will find some." So they cast, and now they were not able to draw it in because of the multitude of the fish . . . . Jesus said to them, "Bring some of the fish which you have just caught . . . . Come and eat breakfast." Yet none of the disciples dared ask Him, "Who are You?"—knowing that it was the Lord. Jesus then came and took the bread and gave it to them, and likewise the fish.

John 21:4-13

On two occasions after His Resurrection, Jesus shared a meal of fish with His Disciples. Because of this, the early Christians chose the fish as a symbol of their faith. While the Disciples were able to see and touch Jesus to prove that He had indeed risen to life, their real faith came from their belief in the truth and goodness of Jesus and His promises. To have faith is to believe in Jesus, to rely on Him and to have trust in Him even though we have not seen Him. Through our faith, we as Christians share in Jesus' Resurrection.

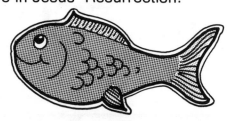

SS842

THE MAN ON THE SHORE

Each space in the puzzle picture below has a number and a letter in it. Find the letters that fit on the lines below to find out what the man on the shore said.

One night about a week after the Resurrection, Peter and six of the Disciples took a boat and some nets out onto the lake to fish, but they didn't catch any. When dawn came, they saw a man standing on the shore. When they told the man that they didn't have any fish, he said,

" ___ ___ ___ ___   ___ ___ ___   ___ ___ ___   ___ ___   ___ ___ ___   ___ ___ ___ ___ ___
   10 25 24 6   6 1 20   18 20 6   26 18   6 1 20   16 11 22 1 6

___ ___ ___ ___   ___ ___   ___ ___ ___   ___ ___ ___ ___   AND YOU WILL FIND SOME."
24 11 7 20   26 14   6 1 20   3 26 25 6

Find out what the secret picture is by coloring in all the spaces that contain letters from the words below.

**PEACE
BE
WITH
YOU.**

Who did the Disciples see on the shore of the lake?

_____

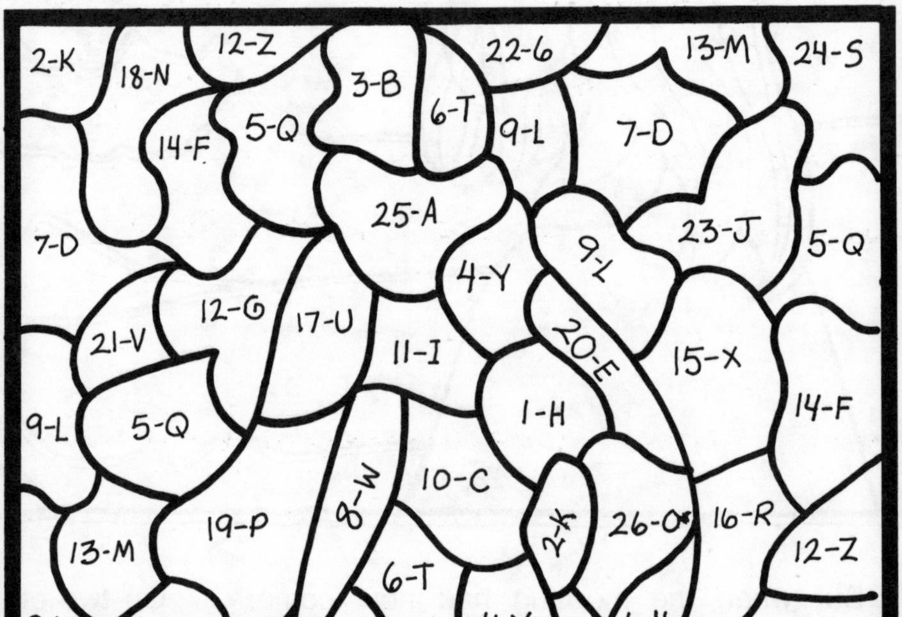

BREAKFAST BY THE SEA

Read John 21:1-14. If the sentence below is true, color the square in the TRUE column. If it is false, color the square in the FALSE column. Print the letters in the uncolored squares on the numbered lines. If your answers are correct, the letters will spell out John's words when he saw Jesus on the shore.

	TRUE	FALSE
1	S	I
2	T	O
3	H	I
4	S	A
5	T	V
6	E	H
7	E	F
8	L	A
9	I	O
10	T	R
11	D	H

1. The Disciples were fishing at a place called Tiberias.
2. It was Nathanael's idea to go fishing.
3. The men fished all night but didn't catch any fish.
4. When the Disciples saw the man on the shore, they knew it was Jesus.
5. When Jesus asked, ''Have you caught anything,'' the Disciples lied.
6. Jesus told them to cast the net on the right side of the boat.
7. When the Disciples threw the net into the water, the net ripped.
8. Peter rowed the boat full of fish to the shore.
9. Jesus made a fire of coals to cook the fish on.
10. Jesus and the Disciples ate bread and fish for breakfast.
11. This was the first time Jesus appeared to the Disciples after He was raised from the dead.

JOHN TOLD PETER, ''___ ___   ___ ___   ___ ___ ___   ___ ___ ___ ___!''
   1 2   3 4   5 6 7   8 9 10 11

Color the spaces with this fish 🐟 red.
Color the spaces with this fish 🐠 blue.   How many fish did the Disciples catch?_____

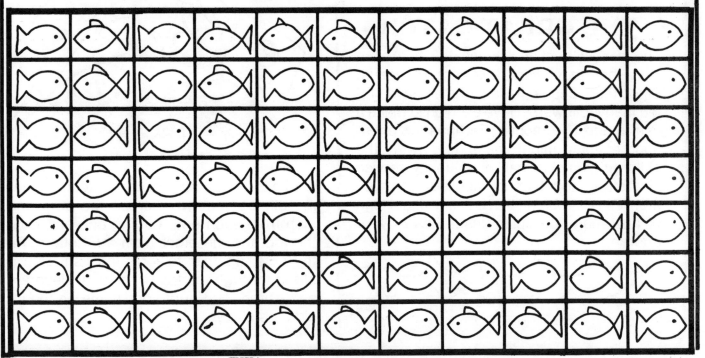

Shining Star Publications, Copyright © 1987, A division of Good Apple, Inc.   SS842

CHRISTIANITY—A FISH STORY

When Jesus appeared to the Disciples in the Upper Room the evening of His Resurrection, they thought He was a ghost. Even though He showed them His hands and feet, they still did not believe. To rid them of their doubts about His Resurrection and show that He was really alive, Jesus ate a meal of fish and honeycomb with the Disciples.

FISHING WITH JESUS

Fish are often mentioned in the New Testament in connection with Jesus. Have the children "go fishing" in Scripture to "catch" as many references to fish as they can. Have each child write a paragraph and draw a picture about a fishing event in Scripture on a white fish shape. Arrange the fish and a picture of Jesus in a display along with the caption "Fishing with Jesus."

FISHERS OF MEN

Seven of the Apostles were fishermen by occupation, but Jesus called all of them to be "fishers of men." Talk about what this meant the Disciples were to do. Jesus asks each of us to be a fisherman too. Have each child draw and cut out a fish on which he has printed his name. Attach a paper clip to the tail of each fish. Make a "fish pond." Each week, let each child use a fishing pole with a magnet "hook" to catch a fish. During the week, the children should make a special effort to bring joy to those whose names they have "caught."

THE GREAT CATCH

The early Christians chose the fish as a sign that they were followers of Jesus. Since then, Jesus' fishers of men have netted many followers. Have each child make a fish to add to a mobile. Perhaps the entire congregation might make fish (with the children's help) as part of a Sunday service and string together in mobiles. The fish mobiles could be displayed as a visual sign of how many disciples Jesus has in your church.

Fold a 2" x 12" strip of construction paper in half. Cut halfway across the strip one inch from each end, cutting one end from the top and the other from the bottom. Fit the cuts together to form the fish. Run a string through the top of the fish. Decorate as desired, and print your name on the inside, as shown.

SS842

SIGNS OF THE FISH

To the early Christians, the fish was a symbol of the Eucharist and of Christianity in general. Because Jesus shared several meals of fish with the Disciples after the Resurrection, the Disciples came to think of the fish as a sign that Jesus is with us. When the early Christians in Rome had to go underground to practice their faith, they carved the sign of the fish on the catacomb walls. If possible, find some pictures of the catacombs to show the students.

FISH PINS AND STICKERS

The children might enjoy designing their own signs of the fish to proclaim that they are Christians. A fish pin can be made from styrofoam, following the directions for the lamb pendant on page 67. The fish may be colored with markers before shrinking and glued to a safety pin after it is finished. A fish sticker for a bicycle can also be created. Simply draw a colored fish with water-base markers on a small piece of white paper. Cut a piece of clear Con-Tact paper slightly larger than the sign. Put the fish upside-down in the center of the Con-Tact paper. Stick it on your bike.

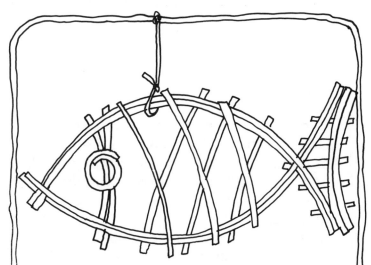

SPAGHETTI FISH SYMBOL

Spaghetti can be used to create an interesting fish as a symbol of Christianity. For each fish, cook about 20 pieces of long spaghetti for eight minutes. Drain and rinse the spaghetti to remove any excess starch. Tint ¼ cup white glue with food coloring. Put some spaghetti into the glue and swirl it around until it is well coated. Draw a simple fish shape on a piece of aluminum foil. (The Christian fish symbol has no fins.) Turn up the foil along the edges so the glue won't run off the paper. Put the spaghetti on the foil and form a fish shape. Use two or three pieces of spaghetti to outline the body. Use shorter pieces to make a crisscross design on the body. Be sure that all the spaghetti pieces overlap. Allow the fish to dry for several days. Then carefully peel away the foil. Add a string and hang the fish in a window.

When light shines through it, the fish has a stained-glass appearance. For an interesting effect, try combining different colors of spaghetti. Pastel colors work best.

STYROFOAM PATTERN

EGGSHELL MOSAIC FISH

Jesus called His Disciples to be fishers of men. Their mission did not end when Jesus returned to heaven. The Disciples continued on, drawing more and more people into the net of Christianity. The children might enjoy making special fishing scenes to remind them that they too are called to follow Jesus and spread His message to others.

Duplicate the fish pattern for each child. Give him these directions: Cut the fish out of cardboard. Wash and dry an eggshell, and crush it lightly between two pieces of paper. (The crushed pieces should not be too small.) Coat the dotted part of the body with glue, and stick on the eggshell pieces to resemble scales. Add a piece of shell for the mouth. Paint the entire fish one color. Coat with clear shellac, and add a movable eye. Glue the fish to an underwater scene. Add a real string and wire hook. Print an appropriate Bible verse or a line from a song on the scene.

FISH PATTERN

CREATIVE CARDBOARD FISH

Attractive fish can also be made from corrugated cardboard. Duplicate the fish pattern on thin paper, giving each child a copy. Trace a fish onto cardboard and cut it apart in sections to use as patterns. Mark the direction of the ribbing on each section. The children can then use these patterns to cut out the necessary fish sections from corrugated cardboard. Have them paint the tails and mid-body sections one color and the rest of the sections a second color. Have each glue his fish together on the thin paper pattern, and when it is dry, trim away the excess paper. Each child can add his fish to a bulletin board scene for an attractive classroom display. Add an appropriate Bible verse or other saying for a finishing touch.

SS842

JESUS VISITS HIS FRIENDS

After He died and rose to life again, Jesus came back to see the Disciples several different times. During the forty days Jesus spent on Earth between His Resurrection and His Ascension to Heaven, Jesus appeared to His friends on nine different occasions (not including the Ascension). Organize the children into eight groups. Assign each group to a different appearance. Younger children might create roller box stories based on the Scripture passages. Older children could choose to present newscasts or press conferences (see below).

Jesus' appearances:

> To Mary Magdalene (Mark 16:9-11; John 20:11-18)
> To the group of women (Matthew 28:9,10)
> To Peter (Luke 24:34; John 21:15-19)
> To the two Disciples on the way to Emmaus (Mark 16:12,13; Luke 24:13-35)
> To the ten Apostles in Jerusalem without Thomas (Luke 24:36-43, John 20:19-23)
> To the eleven, including Thomas (John 20:24-29, Mark 16:14-18)
> To the seven Apostles on the lake in Galilee (John 21:1-14)
> To the five hundred in Galilee (Matthew 28:16-20, I Corinthians 15:6)
> To James (I Corinthians 15:7)—We don't know what happened this time, but a ninth group of children might write an imaginary account of this appearance based on what they know about Jesus and James.

ROLLER BOX STORY

Make a roller box from a small empty box. Cut holes for the dowels in the sides and a window in the front. Insert dowels at the top and bottom of the box. Cut a long strip of paper the width of the window. Mark the paper into sections the length of the window. Draw scenes showing the events of Christ's appearance. Allow space to write the story (in your own words) below each picture. If you like, add a title and credits section. Tape the picture strip to the dowels so that the story can be presented by rolling the top dowel to move the paper strip.

NEWSCASTS

Role play a news broadcast relating the story of Jesus' appearances. Set up an area to resemble a TV newsroom, complete with call letters (FISH) and an anchorperson. Provide on-the-spot reporting, news photo, etc., to make the newscast seem realistic.

PRESS CONFERENCE

Choose members of your group (and other children if needed) to play the roles of the friends of Jesus. Choose others to play the roles of reporters. Make name cards for the reporters and the news media they represent. Prepare questions for Jesus' friends which might be asked at a press conference. Present the press conference for the class. Remember that reporters always identify themselves to the persons they are addressing and the TV, radio station or newspaper magazine they work for.

SS842

PEACE BE WITH YOU

We think of Easter as a joyful time, but for the Disciples that first Easter was frightening and confusing. Frightened by the events of the last few days and fearing that they too might be arrested and put to death, the Disciples hid in the upper room in Jerusalem where they had shared a Passover meal with Jesus the night before He died. Jesus' first words when He appeared to His followers were ''Peace be with you.'' He understood their fears and worries and did not want them to be afraid.

Like the Apostles, Jesus does not want us to be afraid. He wants us to know that God is always with us. Have the children find or draw pictures of things children their age worry about. Make a large cardboard collage in the shape of a fish. Print the phrase ''Peace be with you'' on the fish. Talk about the ways God is with us even though we may not recognize His presence. The fish can be a reminder to the children that even in the midst of our fears and worries, the Lord is there to help and guide us.

''. . . I want you to be without care . . . .''
I Corinthians 7:32

Jesus does not want us to worry or be afraid. Have each child write his biggest worry on a paper. Suggest that he try to let go of his worry by turning it over to God and letting Him handle it. To make the experience a more tangible one, have the child take his paper into church and place it on the altar as a sign that he is turning his problem over to the Lord. Read Acts 2:25,26,28 to conclude the service.

God is near! Create a cartoon strip to show how you know God is there to help and guide you in times of trouble.

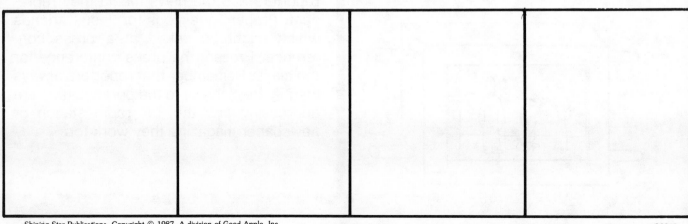

SS842

THE UPPER ROOM

On that first Easter evening, Jesus appeared to ten of His Apostles in an upper room in Jerusalem, the same room in which they had gathered for the Last Supper. At first the Disciples thought Jesus was a ghost because the door was locked. After He had talked with them and shared a meal of fish and honeycomb, they believed and were full of joy. Later they told Thomas, who was not present, "We have seen the Lord." Thomas did not believe them.

Choose one child to be Thomas. Send him on an errand for a few minutes. While he is gone, read Luke 24:36-42 to the other children. When "Thomas" returns, have the other children pretend to be Apostles and describe the event to Thomas as if it had actually happened to them. If they were Thomas, would they have believed? Read John 20:25-29.

Thomas is usually remembered as "doubting Thomas," yet he was not the only Disciple who needed to see before he could believe. Have the children read John 20:1-10 to discover two others who doubted.

THOMAS AND I

Although he needed to see Jesus before he believed, Thomas was essentially a man of faith. Read John 11:16 and John 20:27-29. Sometimes we are like Thomas. Sometimes our faith is strong; at other times it is weak. Ask each child to share a time (in writing or orally) when he is like Thomas.

I am like doubting Thomas when

_____

I am like Thomas, the man of faith, when

_____

I KNOW JESUS LIVES!

Jesus appeared to His Disciples not only to prove that He was alive, but also to convince them to carry His peace to all people. We have not seen Jesus like Thomas did. How do we know that He lives? Have each child write a story showing how we can bring Jesus' peace to others and show them that Jesus lives in our hearts. What signs of the risen Lord can we give to others to help them to be witnesses to the Resurrection?

SS842

WALK BY FAITH

What is faith? Find out what the Gospels tell us by solving the puzzles.

Each word in this Scripture verse can be found in the word search. Words are printed across or down. Use the number of spaces for each word in the verse as a clue to help you find the word in the word search. Print the words on the lines below.

	1	2	3	4	5	6	7	8	9
A	P	W	M	A	Y	T	H	A	T
B	B	I	S	J	W	Z	A	N	D
C	E	T	H	E	Y	T	H	A	T
D	L	H	P	S	O	N	Z	Q	I
E	I	E	X	U	U	G	O	D	N
F	E	H	I	S	F	Q	F	K	A
G	V	A	C	H	R	I	S	T	M
H	E	V	M	A	Y	L	I	F	E
I	B	E	L	I	E	V	I	N	G

. . . THESE ARE WRITTEN THAT YOU   M _ _

B _ _ _ _ _ _ _ _   T _ _ _   J _ _ _ _   I _

T _ _   C _ _ _ _ _ _,   T _ _   S _ _   O _

G _ _,   A _ _   T _ _ _   B _ _ _ _ _ _ _ _

Y _ _   M _ _   H _ _ _   L _ _ _   I _

H _ _ _   N _ _ _ _. (John 20:31)

When Jesus spoke to Thomas after His Resurrection, He told Thomas what faith is. Find out what Jesus said by solving this puzzle. The letters are in the word search above. Use the clue under each space to find the letter. (1B is where column 1 and row B meet.)

1B 6H 4C 7G 3B 2E 9B   4H 5G 9H   6A 7C 5D 7G 1C

2A 2F 7E   2F 4H 6I 1H   6D 5D 8G   3B 4C 2I 8I

2G 8B 9B   5H 5I 9A   7A 2G 1G 5I

1I 2E 6H 3F 1C 1G 4C 9B . (John 20:29)

(Answers are found on page 144.)

FISH MEMORY CHAIN

Enlarge the fish pattern. Fold construction paper in half. Place the mouth of the fish on the fold line. Trace the fish. Cut out the fish (cutting through both layers of paper). Have the children find and memorize Scripture verses about faith. (Hebrews 11 is a good source.) Each time a child learns a verse, he prints his name and the Scripture reference on the fish and adds it to the chain. To assemble the chain, open the first fish and insert half of the second fish through the tail of the first fish. Close the fish. Glue the tail.

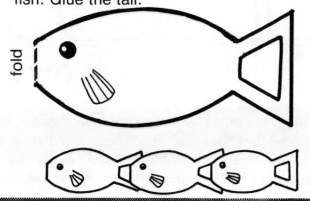

fold

SS842

A NEW APOSTLE

One of the first things Jesus' followers did after Jesus had ascended to Heaven was to choose a new Apostle to take the place of Judas Iscariot. One hundred and twenty disciples gathered together for the important decision. Two disciples were proposed—Barsabbas (Justus) and Matthias. After praying for guidance from the Lord, the disciples cast lots. According to Hebrew custom, the names were written on stones and placed in a vessel. The vessel was then turned over, and the first stone which fell out named the new Apostle—Matthias.

HELP WANTED

Read Acts 1:15-26. What qualifications were necessary for a disciple to be chosen as the twelfth Apostle? Write a ''job opening'' ad for an Apostle to replace Judas.

APOSTLE—To succeed Judas as one of the chosen Twelve.

EXPERIENCE REQUIRED: _____
_____
_____
_____

PERSONAL QUALITIES REQUIRED:
_____
_____
_____
_____

JOB DESCRIPTION: _____
_____
_____
_____
_____
_____

BENEFITS: _____
_____
_____

TO APPLY, CONTACT: _____

CHOOSING AN APOSTLE

We know very little about either Matthias or Barsabbas except that they must have been close to Jesus. Choose one child to play the role of Peter. Divide the other children into two groups—one supporting Matthias and the other in favor of Barsabbas. Allow time for each group to make up some reasons why its candidate should be elected as the twelfth Apostle. Role play the disciples choosing a successor to Judas.

In a way, each one of us has been chosen to be an apostle, to go out into the world and proclaim the good news about Jesus. Have the children suggest ways someone their age can do this.

SS842

NO MORE FEAR

Words and Music by Helen Kitchell Evans
Frances Mann Benson

1. Je-sus lives, Je-sus lives, It is Eas-ter Day. Let a prayer fill the air Easter joy let's share.
2. Let's re-joice, Let's re-joice It is Eas-ter Day. No more fear, for us here, Great joy, it does bring;

From the cross now set free, Free for you and me. Yes, from the cross now set free, Free for you and me.
We can live ev– er more with our Heaven-ly king. Yes, we can live—ev-er-more, With our Heaven-ly king.

SS842

ALLELUIA PEOPLE
A Three-Act Easter Pageant

(See page 143 for tips on costumes, scenery and props.)
—Cast of Characters—

Narrator	Martha
Jesus	Chorus
Apostles	Priests 1, 2
James	Elders 1, 2, 3
Judas	Caiaphas
Disciple 1	Temple Guards
Disciple 2	Angels
Disciple 3	Soldiers
Disciple 4	Girl
John	Servants 1, 2
Peter	Pilate
Andrew	Herod
Boy	Palace Guards
Father	Mary Magdalene
Crowd of People	Mary, the Mother of James
Lazarus	Joanna
Mary	

Setting: A roadway in the city of Jerusalem—A boy and his father sit along the road near one side. Jesus and the Apostles enter and stop before the scenery.

Act I
Scene 1

NARRATOR: It was Sunday, the beginning of Holy Week. Jesus and His friends were coming to Jerusalem for the Jewish Passover festival.

JESUS: Go to the village and bring me the young donkey you will find there. If anyone asks, tell him the Master needs it, but it will be returned.

JAMES:	Yes, Lord. *(He and another Apostle exit and return with the donkey. Jesus sits upon it.)*
NARRATOR:	*(As Jesus rides into the city.)* So Jesus rode into Jerusalem, the Holy City, the city where King David had established his kingdom.
BOY:	*(Pointing to Jesus.)* Who is that man?
FATHER:	He is the one the prophet Zechariah spoke of when he said, ''Look, your King is coming to you! He is humble and rides on a donkey.'' Now, go! Call the people.
BOY:	*(Calling out to the others.)* Jesus of Nazareth is coming! The Son of David comes!
PEOPLE:	*(Come running, carrying palm branches.)* Hosanna! Hosanna to the King! Praise to David's son! *(As Jesus rides through the crowd, all sing ''Sway the Palms'' on page 10. The movements can be performed at this point, if desired.)*
NARRATOR:	As Jesus rode through the city, the crowd welcomed Him as their King and spread their cloaks and palm branches along His path.
JUDAS:	*(Speaking to another Apostle as he watches Jesus move through the crowd.)* See, the people accept Him as their Messiah. Maybe now Jesus will declare Himself the King.
NARRATOR:	*(As Jesus and crowd exit.)* But Jesus did not declare Himself King, for His kingdom was not of this world. The kingdom He had come to establish was a heavenly one. He had not come to be a powerful ruler and lead their fight against the Romans.

Act I
Scene 2

Setting: A home in Bethany. Lazarus, Martha and Mary are working around the house.

NARRATOR:	It was Sunday evening. Jesus and the Disciples had come to the home of Jesus' friends, Lazarus, Martha and Mary, in the village of Bethany. *(Jesus and Disciples enter.)*
JESUS:	*(Hugging Lazarus.)* Lazarus! My friend!
LAZARUS:	Master! It is good to see You!
MARY:	Lord! Welcome to our home again. We've missed You!
MARTHA:	Come in, Lord. You and Your friends are welcome to break bread with us. *(Jesus, Lazarus, and the Disciples sit down at the table; Martha brings them some food and drink;)*
NARRATOR:	While they were eating, Mary went to a shelf and took down a beautiful white alabaster box. The box was filled with an expensive perfume which had been imported from another land.

Shining Star Publications, Copyright © 1987, A division of Good Apple, Inc.
SS842

MARY:	*(Goes up to Jesus as He sits at the table, breaks open the box, and pours the perfume on Jesus' feet, then she wipes His feet with her hair.)*
DISCIPLE 1:	What was the use of wasting the perfume?
DISCIPLE 2:	It could have been sold for more than three hundred silver coins and the money given to the poor! *(Mary looks upset and begins to cry softly.)*
JESUS:	*(Standing suddenly.)* Leave her alone! Why are you bothering her? She has done a fine and beautiful thing for Me. *(The Disciples look sheepish.)* You will always have poor people with you, and any time you want to, you can help them. But you will not always have Me. What Mary did, she did to anoint Me for My burial. *(Places hand on Mary's head.)* Mary, I tell you that wherever people hear of this, they will remember you for your unselfish love.

Act I
Scene 3

Setting: A fig tree in the countryside outside of Bethany. Chorus is at side of stage.

NARRATOR:	It was Monday morning, and Jesus and His Disciples had returned to Jerusalem from Bethany. Jesus saw a fig tree by the side of the road.
JESUS:	Look, here is a fig tree with many leaves. I am hungry. We will gather some figs for our midday meal. *(Goes up to the tree, but does not find any figs.)*
NARRATOR:	Jesus expected to find figs on the tree because of the leaves. A fig tree usually begins to bear fruit before it has leaves.
JESUS:	*(To tree.)* You will never again bear fruit!
DISCIPLES:	*(Amazed.)* Lord, look. The fig tree has dried up!
CHORUS:	*(Sing "The Fig Tree" on page 51.)*
DISCIPLE 3:	Lord, why did this tree dry up so quickly?
JESUS:	Have faith in God. If you believe that what you say will happen, it will be done for you. Remember this: A tree is known by its fruit. *(The Disciples look confused.)* I have chosen you to go and bear much fruit, the kind of fruit that lasts. And so the Father will give you whatever you ask of Him in My name.
DISCIPLE 4:	But, Lord. How are we to bring forth fruit that will last?
JESUS:	This, then, I command you: love one another. You will be known by your fruits, by the things that you do.

 SS842

Act I
Scene 4

Setting: Palace of Caiaphas, the high priest. Guards stand near entrance. Rest sit around table.

NARRATOR: The chief priests and elders had met together at the palace of the high priest, Caiaphas. They made plans to arrest Jesus secretly and put Him to death.

PRIEST 1: The time has come to act. We must wait no longer.

ELDER 1: True. But what about the crowds of people who follow Him?

CAIAPHAS: We must not do it during the festival or the people will riot.

ELDER 2: We must arrest Him at night.

ELDER 3: In a place away from the crowds.

PRIEST 2: Yes. Once He is a prisoner of Rome, the people will not stand by Him.

CAIAPHAS: *(To the guards.)* Time is short! Have you found out where He stays at night?

GUARDS: *(Sheepishly.)* No, Sir.

JUDAS: *(Entering.)* What will you give me if I betray Jesus to you?

CAIAPHAS: *(Counts out thirty silver coins, puts them in bag, hands it to Judas.)* It must be soon!

JUDAS: When the time is right, I will lead you to Him. *(Judas exits.)*

Act I Scene 5

Setting: An upper room in Jerusalem. Jesus and the Apostles are seated at a table. Chorus is off to the side of the stage.

NARRATOR: It was Thursday evening. It was the night of the Jewish feast celebrating the freedom of the Jews from slavery in Egypt. Jesus and His friends were gathered in the upper room of a friend's house to eat the Passover meal. Jesus knew that He was about to be betrayed to His enemies.

JESUS: I have wanted so much to eat this meal with you before I leave you. *(Pauses, looks sadly around at the Apostles.)* But one of you who shares this meal with Me is going to betray Me.

APOSTLES: *(Alarmed.)* Never, Lord! Is it I, Master? Surely, Lord, you don't mean me? *(Etc.)*

JOHN: Who is it, Lord?

JESUS: It is one who dips bread in the dish with me.

JUDAS: Is it I, Lord?

JESUS: So you say. *(Dips bread in dish; hands it to Judas.)* Hurry and do what you must. *(After Judas takes bread and exits.)* My children, I will not be with you much longer. And now I give you a new commandment: You must love one another as I have loved you. By your love, everyone will know that you are my friends.

NARRATOR:	Jesus had been like a shepherd to His friends. He had loved them like a shepherd loves His sheep. He was willing to give His life for them.
CHORUS:	*(Sing ''Our Loving Shepherd'' on page 69.)*
PETER:	Lord, where are You going?
JESUS:	Where I am going now you cannot follow Me. Later, you will follow Me.
PETER:	Lord, why can't I follow You now? I would go to prison or even die for You!
JESUS:	Peter. Peter. Before the rooster crows, you will say three times that you do not know Me. *(Takes bread, blesses it, breaks it and gives a piece to each Apostle.)* Take this and eat. This is My body which is given for you. Do this in remembrance of Me. *(Takes the cup of wine and lifts it toward Heaven.)* This is My blood which will be shed for the forgiveness of sins. I will never drink this wine again until I drink the new wine with you in My Father's kingdom.
NARRATOR:	Then they sang a hymn and went out to the Mount of Olives.
APOSTLES & CHORUS:	*(Sing ''The Passover Song'' on page 62.)*

Act II
Scene 1

Setting: Garden of Gethsemane

NARRATOR:	Jesus had come to the Garden of Gethsemane to pray. Peter, James and John were with Him. *(Jesus and Disciples enter.)*
JESUS:	*(To Disciples.)* Stay here and watch while I pray.
NARRATOR:	The Disciples sat and soon fell asleep. Jesus went farther into the garden and knelt to pray.
JESUS:	Abba, My Father! All things are possible for You. Take this cup of suffering away from Me. Yet I will do what You want. *(Gets up, returns to Disciples.)* Peter, are you asleep? Weren't you able to stay awake for even one hour? Keep watch, and pray that you will not fall into temptation.
NARRATOR:	Again Jesus went deeper into the garden and knelt to pray. Once more He returned to His friends and found them sleeping. A third time, Jesus returned to His prayers. So great was His suffering that His sweat fell to the ground like great drops of blood.
JESUS:	*(Crying out in anguish.)* Abba! Father! If it can be, take this cup away. *(Angel appears and places hand on Jesus' shoulder.)*
NARRATOR:	An angel from Heaven appeared to Jesus and gave Him strength. Jesus continued praying, asking God for the strength to accept His suffering. *(Angel exits.)*

Shining Star Publications, Copyright © 1987, A division of Good Apple, Inc.
SS842

JESUS:	*(Returning to Disciples.)* Are you still asleep? Get up. The hour has come. My betrayer is near.
JUDAS:	*(Enters with soldiers and chief priests; kisses Jesus on cheek.)* Peace be with You, Teacher!
JESUS:	*(Sadly.)* Judas, do you betray the Son of Man with a kiss?
NARRATOR:	When Judas kissed Him, the soldiers knew Jesus was the one they wanted and rushed forward to arrest Him.
JAMES:	*(Apostles draw swords.)* Shall we use our swords, Lord? *(Peter leaps forward and cuts off ear of a servant.)*
JESUS:	*(To Disciples.)* Put away your swords! Those who take up the sword will die by the sword! *(Turns and touches man's ear.)*
NARRATOR:	Then Jesus touched the wounded man's ear and healed him.
JESUS:	*(Turning to crowd.)* Why do you come for Me with weapons? Every day I sat and taught in the temple, and you did not arrest Me. *(Slight pause.)* But the Scriptures must come true.
NARRATOR:	Hearing this, the Disciples were afraid and ran away. The soldiers tied Jesus' hands and led Him away.

Act II
Scene 2

Setting: Courtyard of Caiaphas' palace—A charcoal fire is burning. Jesus with guards at one end of courtyard. Servants working in different parts of courtyard.

NARRATOR:	The soldiers brought Jesus to the palace of the high priest, Caiaphas. Peter followed at a safe distance. *(Peter enters, tries to keep his face hidden, and stands near the gate.)*
GIRL:	*(Crosses to Peter.)* You, too, were with Jesus.
PETER:	Woman, I don't even know Him. *(Crosses to fire to warm himself.)*
SERVANT 1:	*(Noticing Peter.)* You are one of them too!
PETER:	*(With a little anger in his voice.)* No, I am not!
SERVANT 2:	*(Crosses to fire.)* Of course you are one of Jesus' Disciples! You, too, are from Galilee. You speak like a Galilean!
PETER:	*(Angrily.)* I swear I do not know the man! *(Sound of rooster crowing.)*
NARRATOR:	Just then the rooster crowed. Jesus turned toward Peter and looked at him. *(Pause.)* Then Peter remembered what Jesus had said about betraying Him. Peter left the courtyard and wept bitterly. *(Peter exits in tears.)*

Shining Star Publications, Copyright © 1987, A division of Good Apple, Inc.

SS842

Act II
Scene 3

Setting: Pilate's palace—Herod's palace. The same setting can be used for both palaces by having actors leave from one side of stage and reenter from the other.

NARRATOR: It was early Friday morning. The chief priests had brought Jesus to Pilate, the Roman governor. *(Pilate sits on throne; Jesus, priests and guard stand before him.)*

PRIEST 1: This man is guilty of blasphemy. He says He is Christ the King!

PRIEST 2: We want Him put to death! *(Priests exit.)*

PILATE: Are You the King of the Jews?

JESUS: So you say.

PILATE: Are You a king, then?

JESUS: My kingdom is not of this world.

NARRATOR: *(As Pilate picks up and reads paper thoughtfully.)* Pilate looked over the charges against Jesus. He saw that Jesus was from Galilee, the area ruled over by King Herod, who was in Jerusalem for the festival.

PILATE: *(To guard.)* This man is a Galilean. Take Him to Herod. *(exit.)*

NARRATOR: *(As soldiers, then Jesus and guard, enter from other side of stage.)* So the temple guard took Jesus to Herod's palace and turned Him over to the soldiers. *(Guards exit; Herod enters and sits on throne.)* Herod asked Jesus many questions, but Jesus did not say a word.

HEROD: *(Cruelly.)* So You would be King of the Jews! *(Laughs.)* Well, we will make You king!

NARRATOR: The soldiers put a purple robe around Jesus' shoulders and a crown of thorns on His head.

SOLDIERS: *(Making fun of Jesus.)* Hail, King of the Jews! Hail, King of the Jews!

HEROD: *(Cruelly.)* Take this king back to Pilate! *(Herod exits; Pilate, then Jesus and soldiers enter from other side of stage.)*

NARRATOR: It was the custom at the time of Passover to set one prisoner free. *(Crowd enters.)*

PILATE: *(To crowd.)* Who shall I set free? Jesus, who has done nothing wrong? Or the thief, Barabbas?

CROWD: Barabbas! Give us Barabbas!

PILATE: Then what should I do with Jesus?

CROWD: Crucify Him! *(Soldiers take the purple robe off Jesus and lead Him off the stage. Crowd follows.)*

Shining Star Publications, Copyright © 1987, A division of Good Apple, Inc. SS842

Act III
Scene 1

Setting: Sunrise, the tomb in the garden. The stone is rolled away. (If the stone suggested on page 119 was made, use it.) Chorus off to side of stage.

NARRATOR: It was early on Sunday morning. Mary Magdalene, Mary the mother of James, and Joanna came to the garden bringing sweet spices to place in Jesus' tomb. *(Women enter, walking slowly.)*

MARY J: How will we be able to roll the stone away from the door of the tomb?

JOANNA: I don't know. The stone is very heavy.

MARY M: Look! The tomb is open!

NARRATOR: The women reached the tomb and looked inside. *(Angel enters from side or from behind the stone.)* They saw a young man clothed in white, and they were afraid.

ANGEL: Do not be afraid. You are looking for Jesus of Nazareth, who was crucified. He is not here. He is risen. Go tell the Disciples.

NARRATOR: Trembling with fear, the women ran from the tomb. *(Mary J and Joanna exit as Peter and John enter and stand at the side of the stage.)*

MARY M: *(Weeping to Peter and John.)* They have taken the Lord from the tomb. We don't know where they have put Him! *(Exits.)*

NARRATOR: Peter and John rushed to the tomb. John ran faster and arrived there first. Overcome with emotion, he did not go inside. Peter joined him, and they entered the tomb.

JOHN: *(In awe.)* Mary was right! Jesus is not here!

PETER: Look, there are the linen cloths they wrapped Him in. But His body is gone!

JOHN: What can this mean? Could Jesus have risen from the dead? *(Shaking their heads in wonder, the two exit.)*

CHORUS: (Sing ''Roll the Stone Away'' on page 116.)

NARRATOR: A little later Mary Magdalene was standing by the open tomb, crying. *(Angels enter from side or behind stone and sit.)* Looking inside, she saw two angels sitting where the body of Jesus had been, one at the head and the other at the feet.

ANGELS: *(Gently.)* Lady, why are you crying?

MARY M: They have taken my Lord away, and I do not know where they have put Him. *(Jesus enters and stands behind Mary. Mary turns around and sees Him. Angels exit.)*

 SS842

MARY M:	If you have taken Him away, sir, please tell me where He is!
JESUS:	*(With emphasis.)* Mary!
NARRATOR:	When Mary heard her name, she knew that it was Jesus! She knelt to kiss His feet.
MARY M:	*(In a voice full of wonder and love.)* My Lord!
JESUS:	*(Gently touching her head.)* Do not cling to me, Mary. I have not yet gone back up to the Father. Go and tell my brothers.
NARRATOR:	So Mary Magdalene went and told the Disciples that she had seen the Lord, but they did not believe her.

Act III Scene 2

Setting: An upper room in Jerusalem—Apostles are sitting around, frightened.

NARRATOR:	It was Sunday evening. Thomas was not here. The other Apostles were hiding in the upper room where they had shared the Passover meal with Jesus. They had locked the doors because they were afraid of the Jewish authorities. Jesus had been crucified, and they feared that they, too, might be arrested. *(Jesus enters.)* Suddenly they looked up and saw Jesus standing in their midst.
JESUS:	Peace be with you.
NARRATOR:	For a moment, they were too terrified to speak. They thought they were seeing a ghost!
JESUS:	Why are you afraid? Why do you doubt? *(Holds out His hands.)* Look at My hands and My feet, and see that it is I, Myself. Feel Me, and you will know, for a ghost doesn't have flesh and bones, as you can see I have. *(The Apostles gather around Him and touch His hands and feet.)*
NARRATOR:	The Apostles were filled with joy and wonder, but they still could not believe Jesus lived.
JESUS:	Do you have anything to eat?
ANDREW:	*(Handing Jesus a piece of fish.)* We have some fish, Lord.
NARRATOR:	Great joy filled the hearts of the Apostles as they watched Jesus eat the fish. Ghosts do not eat. Now they knew that Jesus truly lived. They were no longer afraid.
JESUS:	Truly I tell you, I will be with you always, even to the end of time.
ENTIRE CAST:	*(Sing ''No More Fear'' on page 132.)*

CURTAIN

COSTUMES

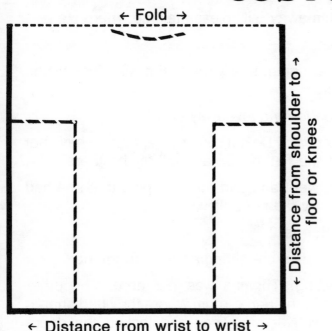

← Fold →

← Distance from shoulder to floor or knees →

← Distance from wrist to wrist →

Simple robes can be made from old sheets or other fabric. Fold the fabric in half, and cut according to the measurements shown at the left. Cut out a neckhole large enough to fit over the child's head with ease. The robe can simply be tied at the waist with a fabric or rope belt, allowing the top to have a blouson effect. Another option is to create the fabric sleeves by stitching as indicated by the dotted lines, allowing plenty of room for armholes, and cutting away the excess. Robes can be made from any color fabric, or designs can be drawn on white ones with fabric crayons or markers. Old bathrobes can also be used. Shoes can be sandals of any type, even beach thongs.

Headwear may also be simple. A long rectangular piece of fabric can be wrapped around the head as shown, or stitched into a simple hood and secured shepherd-style with a headband. Angels can wear circlets of gold or silver Christmas tree tinsel rope, and their robes can also be trimmed with it. A circlet braided from heavy rope or made from grapevines can be used as a crown of thorns.

HEADWEAR

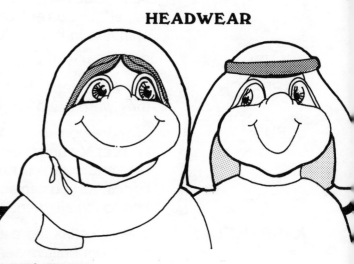

SCENERY

Scenery and props may also be kept simple. Scenery can be painted on large sheets of white paper and suspended from the ceiling, but my preference is to project slides on a white sheet hung behind the actors. (Slides need to be projected from an angle so as not to shine directly on the children.) If you have access to slides of the Holy Land, use them. You can also shoot your own slides of pictures in books or magazines (or pictures drawn by the children). Check with your local high school or a nearby university to see if they have the photographic equipment necessary to shoot close-ups.

Keep props minimal because the scenes are short. The most elaborate prop you will need is a donkey for the first scene. Attach a cardboard head and a rope tail to a sawhorse which has been secured to a platform with wheels. The donkey can be pulled (by means of a rope) across the stage by a child while Jesus sits on it.

SS842

JESUS SAYS GOODBYE

So then, after the Lord had spoken unto them, He was received up into heaven, and sat down at the right hand of God.
And they went out, and preached everywhere, the Lord working with them, and confirming the word through the accompanying signs. Amen.   Mark 16:19,20

When Jesus said farewell to His friends before His Ascension to heaven, He probably said, "Shalom," the Hebrew word meaning "Peace be with you." That is the same greeting He used when He appeared to His Disciples after the resurrection. This is not the end of the Easter story. It is continued in THE ACTS OF THE APOSTLES, and it is going on today.

SS842

ANSWER KEY

WELCOME JESUS p. 7
1. David was the King of Israel, the ancestor of Jesus.
2. A royal king, wearing a crown and riding a war horse
3. The Messiah, the King of the Jews
4. Laying palm branches on His path
5. Hosanna
6. Answers will vary
7. Answers will vary (disappointed)
8. Lays his branch in front of Jesus
9. He wears no royal garb and is riding a donkey.
10. He sees the crown of light around Jesus' head.

PALM TREE FACTS p. 12
1. grows		7. pounds
2. trunk		8. seed
3. feathers		9. color
4. fruit		10. dried
5. flowers		11. long
6. date		12. sweet

JESUS IN THE TEMPLE p. 16
1. miles		11. market
2. gifts		12. worship
3. children		13. power
4. animals		14. drove
5. bought		15. tables
6. coins		16. Scriptures
7. cheated		17. prayer
8. Palm		18. nations
9. sacrifices		19. temple
10. shops		

REBUILDING THE TEMPLE p. 17
The temple of His body would be destroyed, but in three days He would rise up again.

SPRING CLEANING TIME p. 18
1. cheating		4. jealousy
2. lying		5. stealing
3. mean words		6. fighting

GET TO KNOW YOUR HOUSE OF PRAYER p. 19
The hidden objects are Bible, organ, cross, stained glass window, Sunday bulletin, and chalice.

JESUS VISITS BETHANY p. 26
Jesus, Bethany, Mary, Martha, Lazarus, Jesus, house, Jesus, Lazarus, Mary, feet, Martha, house, Jesus, Bethany, Jesus, table, Lazarus, Martha, Mary, box, feet, hair, coins, Jesus, Mary

THE PARABLE OF A SEED p. 45
1. Answers will vary
2. to be a beautiful tree
3. She was alone and did not know how to become a tree.
4. Answers will vary
5. She became buried in the soil.
6. Her coat cracked open.
7. They helped her grow stronger so she could push her way up through the soil.
8. Answers will vary (Possible answer: they will need to grow and change.)
9. Answers will vary
10. Answers will vary (The seed had to "die" before it could become a tree.)

JESUS AND THE WHEAT p. 47
seed, ground, sunshine, weeds, wheat, die, burn, tall, Lord, love

BREAD SYMBOL OF JESUS p. 54
Bethlehem   House of Bread

THEY'LL KNOW WE ARE CHRISTIANS p. 71
If you have love for one another, everyone will know that you are my friends.

JESUS' PRAYER p. 77
I do not pray for these alone but also for those who will believe in Me through their word.

HIDDEN APOSTLES p. 84
Simon (rock near Jesus), James (sleeve), Matthew (hem), Thomas (behind Jesus), Thaddeus & John (large tree at left), Peter & Andrew (bushy trees), Bartholomew & Philip (large tree at right), James (trunk), Judas (wall)

TREASURE IN HEAVEN p. 87
The second Disciple is Judas.

OUR COUNTRY'S COINS p. 90
Liberty—In God We Trust
Penny—Abraham Lincoln—freed the slaves.
Nickel—Thomas Jefferson—wrote the Declaration of Independence to help make our nation free.
Dime—Franklin Roosevelt—known as the friend and protector of the common man; admired for his personal courage when crippled.
Quarter—George Washington—led the fight for freedom, first president.
Half-Dollar—John Kennedy—first Catholic president; noted for his efforts to establish world peace.

THE ROOSTER CROWED p. 94
1. rooster		6. wept
2. servant		7. Galilean
3. looked		8. Luke
4. priest		9. Peter
5. fire		10. three

THE PRODIGAL SON p. 96
1. goods		7. sinned
2. wasted		8. calf
3. famine		9. feast
4. swine		10. angry
5. father		11. alive
6. kissed		FORGIVENESS

BE A CHICKEN "EGGS"-PERT p. 98
1. people		8. eggshell
2. rooster		9. feathers
3. hen		10. parents
4. egg		11. hatched
5. warm		12. down
6. yolk		13. laying
7. beak		

THE LORD LIVES! p. 112
1. third		10. alive
2. Magdalene		11. cross
3. Joanna		12. life
4. Mary		13. eleven
5. Jesus		14. Peter
6. stone		15. amazed
7. body		16. happy
8. two		17. end
9. dead		18. heaven

THE MAN ON THE SHORE p. 122
"Cast the net on the right side of the boat."—Jesus

BREAKFAST BY THE SEA p. 123
1-T, 2-F, 3-T, 4-F, 5-F, 6-T
7-F, 8-F, 9-T, 10-T, 11-F
"It is the Lord!"
153 fish

WALK BY FAITH p. 130
". . . may believe that Jesus is the Christ, the Son of God, and that believing you may have life in His name."

"Blessed are those who have not seen and yet have believed."

Shining Star Publications, Copyright © 1987, A division of Good Apple, Inc.

SS842